Gilberto de Mello Freyre was born at Recife
(Pernambuco) on March 15, 1900. He
studied under private tutors and at the
Colegio Americano Gilreath in his native city.
In 1920 he took a Bachelor of Arts degree at
Baylor University in Waco, Texas, and in
1922 an M.A. at Columbia University, where he
did graduate work under Franz Boas, Franklin
Henry Giddings, Carlton J. H. Hayes, and
Edwin R. A. Seligman.

Freyre has been visiting professor or
lecturer at many of the leading universities
of Europe and America—among them Leland
Stanford, Princeton, Columbia, Michigan,
San Marcos (Lima), Coimbra (Portugal),
King's College (London), the Sorbonne,
Heidelberg, Berlin, Cologne, Hamburg, Bonn,
and Indiana. Freyre was a member in 1946 of
the National Assembly that drew up the
constitution of Brazil. From 1946 to 1950
he served in the Chamber of Deputies and on
its Committee on Cultural and Educational
Matters. In 1949 he was a delegate with
the rank of ambassador from Brazil to the
General Assembly of the United Nations.

Earlier books by Gilberto Freyre
published in English include
The Masters and the Slaves (1946; 1956);
New World in the Tropics (1959);
and *The Mansions and the Shanties (1963).*

ALSO BY *Gilberto Freyre*

The Mansions and the Shanties:
  The Making of Modern Brazil (Sobrados e Mucambos), 1963
New World in the Tropics, 1959
The Masters and the Slaves:
  *A Study in the Development of Brazilian Civilization
    (Casa-Grande & Senzala)*, 1946, 1956

These are Borzoi Books,
  published in New York by Alfred A. Knopf

MOTHER AND SON

MOTHER AND SON

A Brazilian Tale

by GILBERTO FREYRE

Translated from the Portuguese
by Barbara Shelby

New York: ALFRED A. KNOPF

1967

THIS IS A *Borzoi Book*, PUBLISHED BY ALFRED A. KNOPF, INC.

First American Edition

Library of Congress Catalog Card Number: 67–11135

Manufactured in the United States of America

Originally published in Portuguese as *Dona Sinhá e o Filho
Padre* by Livraria José Olympio Editôra S.A.

MOTHER AND SON

1

"YOU ARE insulting my name. One doesn't do that to a lady."

Dona Sinhá was speaking to me. There was a sudden sharpness in her voice, which had at first sounded relaxed, even drawling, like that of all true Wanderleys—so much so that it reminded me of the speech of certain old ladies in my own family.

This asperity in her voice contrasted with the soft expression of her eyes: eyes of the kind that seem never to grow old along with the rest of the body, a trait that seems to be more common among Oriental women—and men—than among Occidentals. There was, indeed, a touch of the Orient in the blond iaiá [1] from Serinhaém, perhaps a remote hint of Amerindian blood.

"But Dona Sinhá," I ventured to say, "when I imagined that story—"

She interrupted me incisively: "You imagined nothing of the kind. You had no business making up a story about my life and trying to be a novelist—did you think I didn't know?—at my expense. You know very well that I exist." (I mentally completed this rather Pascalian thought of Dona Sinhá: I must be aware that she had existed before I had imagined her; if she had not, I would not have tried to conjure her up.)

It was very disconcerting. I had been summoned to this meeting with a lady who wished to discuss "a matter of mutual interest" by a note written in a slightly tremulous hand, delivered by a little Negro boy of such inky blackness that he looked like a servant from a tale by José de Alencar. The note contained the lady's address but not her name: a house in the Square of São José do Ribamar.

I went, feeling rather puzzled. But São José had always attracted me. I have never been able to forget, from my adolescent days, its girls dressed in mourning, nor its houses—to me the most Brazilian of houses—where as recently as a few years ago the month of May was still not only a religious but also a social ritual; where the best munguzá [2] in Recife was cooked on Sunday mornings,

[1] Plantation owner's wife or daughter; "Missy."
[2] Cornmeal mush, flavored with cinnamon.

4

and a rich smell of corn and cinnamon floated out to the street from every house.

Even today, the Square of São José do Ribamar is my favorite corner of São José. It might be said of the entire district that it is not only a space set apart from all others in Recife, but a different time as well. A more backward time, say the lovers of progress, with some disdain.

What could she want of me, this lady who had summoned me with a note written in the hand of a former pupil in a convent school run by French nuns and delivered by a pickaninny who looked like a relic of another age himself? What could the "matter of mutual interest" be? Perhaps she thought I was a collector and had some antique that she wanted to sell—some piece of jacarandá [3] furniture or old silver that she intended to offer me. I had the reputation of being a collector in those days —I, who have always hated collectors, while recognizing them as one of the so-called "necessary evils."

The house was a true São José house. It was modest, certainly, but with a sober dignity closer to poverty than to wealth; poor with a touch of nobility. The little darky whose acquaintance I had already made came to open the door for me. I asked him what his name was, almost sure that it would be Benedito. [4] I was wrong, though; he told me with a good-natured smile that his name was Amaro.

Old chairs stood in the drawing room. Were they made

---

[3] A valuable tropical hardwood of exceptionally beautiful grain.
[4] A common name among Brazilian Negroes, after the Sicilian saint and Franciscan monk of African parentage (1525-89).

of vinhático [5] or jacarandá? Vinhático—the good kind that is by no means inferior to jacarandá, except to the *nouveaux riches*, converts when it comes to antique furniture and therefore fanatically attached to jacarandá, which they sometimes call "holy wood."

I saw no unusually fine piece of furniture, no silver plate, no porcelain characteristic of a conventional Brazilian drawing room at the turn of the century. On the walls hung a couple of antique portraits in oils, by Béraud, perhaps—no signature was visible—which I concluded must represent the lady's parents. On a console table was a yellowed photograph of a seminary student with a face that was more girlish than boyish. Next to the picture stood a vase of flowers—fresh flowers—which had been placed there with an instinct that was part maternal and part devout. There was another photograph on the antique console, this one of a scholarly looking young man with curling moustaches and a pince-nez.

My hostess did not keep me waiting long. "Dona Sinhá'll be here in a minute," said Amaro as he opened the door. It was a Dona Sinhá who had written to me, then. But Brazil was full of Dona Sinhás! Which one was this?

Neither tall nor short and of almost Nordic fairness, with a pince-nez hanging by a black ribbon, the lady who appeared in the dark hallway was a slender person who did not lack, nevertheless, a certain authoritative vigor in the way she held herself erect and in the tone of voice,

[5] A wine-colored tropical hardwood.

relaxed but positive, in which she immediately invited me, to make myself at home in her house. All in all, the ensemble formed by the house, the furniture, and now by the old iaiá who appeared before me with something pleasantly familiar in her bearing, her figure, and her voice, gave me an odd impression of *déjà vu*. At once I began saying to myself: São José never fails; it still has the courage to set itself apart, not only in space but in time, from all other spaces and times in Recife; and not only in Recife, but in Brazil. Exactly: in Brazil.

Dona Sinhá did not appear to be dressed according to the fashion of the day, but to my eyes there was nothing ridiculous or grotesque in her slightly old-fashioned garb. She harmonized perfectly, it seemed to me, with that São José do Ribamar drawing room in which time seemed to have stopped some years before. She made me feel as though I were in a theater-in-the-round functioning for my exclusive benefit—or one in which I were destined to be an actor and not a mere spectator.

It was then that she spoke those sharp words which suddenly deepened the mystery into which I had been drawn: "You are insulting my name!" She even added: "I am not a comedian whose life can be written down for the public to read."

Whereupon she showed me a scrap of newspaper. It was a clipping from a Rio paper in which a columnist announced—too precipitately, as a matter of fact—"the imminent appearance of a novel" of mine, which was to be "the story of Dona Sinhá and her son the priest."

7

"Look at this!" cried Dona Sinhá.

The person addressing me, in that house in São José do Ribamar, was a Dona Sinhá who, having read a journalist's indiscretion regarding a novel by me which was still only a project, and a vague one at that, imagined herself to be the subject of a biography instead of a novel. I thought at once that the good lady might possibly be in need of psychiatric help.

The truth was that I had intended to make a Dona Sinhá, perhaps similar to herself, one of the characters in a sort of novel in which she would appear beside the priest, her son. But now, lo and behold, the fictitious personage assured me that she was not fictitious after all; that she existed. She existed and had been waiting for me, since I had guessed of her existence in my attempt to understand times past, lost in the midst of the present. Suddenly there came to me, with absolute clarity now, the idea suggested by Dona Sinhá herself: that I had in effect only sought her out because she already existed. An idea, I must repeat, which smacked more than a little of Pascal. The Dona Sinhá who had received me in her São José do Ribamar drawing room was not an ignorant woman; from the beginning of her conversation it was obvious that she had learned something from the French nuns. But surely not to the point of being versed in Pascal.

I did not find it easy to adjust to such an unexpected situation: that of finding that "my" Dona Sinhá did, in a way, exist. It was a fantastic situation, after all, even though it was no phantom from another world, but only one from another time, who was laying claim to an existence which turned my idea of a fictitious Dona Sinhá into one that it was necessary to reconsider, at the very least. Well, I reflected, I wasn't born to be the kind of novelist who makes up happenings and characters, but to be a snooper into the intimate depths of human nature, the kind of snooper who pries into real life, or into the realer than real that the French speak of. But how could anything so absurd be possible? How could I possibly have found myself in the presence of a woman who, although a bit antiquated, was certainly real—realer than real —and who began our conversation by assuring me that she was the original of my supposed fictitious creation? And whose image actually did corresopnd almost perfectly to the one I had imagined?

"But Dona Sinhá," I replied cautiously, "how can you be so sure that you are *my* Dona Sinhá? Why should I be insulting your name?"

She did not have to be coaxed into explaining what was, from her point of view, crystal clear. "Why, I'm José Maria's mother. I brought him up to be a priest; I suffered because of him all that you intend to tell about in your book, no doubt. And he suffered because of me all that you have learned, from whom I don't know. When I was told what your book was about, I felt as though my inmost life had been exposed. I tried to forget about it by telling myself that I live so shut away from the world that no one knows I am still alive. Hardly anyone remembers

me any more, and José Maria lives on in this world only
in my adoration of him. But the saints in Heaven know
that he was a saint too. The truth is, I should have died
years ago. I don't know myself how a Dona Sinhá still
lives on in this house here in São José, so different from
what it was when I was a girl. But since the newspapers
made a point of announcing your book, I decided to write
that note asking you to come here as a great favor to me.
And what I beg of you is that you write about someone
and something else and leave me in peace—me and José
Maria, who is dead now, and his friend, who must still be
living somewhere in Europe—and forget about all those
old stories that can be of no interest to a stranger."

I could not help rising to my feet in wonder and
amazement. "The Frenchman" too! That is, the very
same third person I had intended to create, who was to be
a Frenchified Brazilian known to his old schoolfellows in
Recife as "the Frenchman."

It was simply astonishing. What in the world was happening here? Was it a psychic phenomenon of the kind
the English have been studying for years, in their phlegmatic way, without ever coming to any conclusions? No
one had ever mentioned this living Dona Sinhá to me, nor
the story of her life, nor José Maria. I had made it all up.

Well, then, I make up a Dona Sinhá and her religious
son and have everything take place in São José do Ribamar and Serinhaém, in Olinda and Europe, to characters
in a novel that will be a little different from other novels
—and who should turn up but a Dona Sinhá who was

realer than real, getting on in years but still lucid enough, speaking the correct Portuguese of a lady who, though born on an out-of-the-way plantation and saying "chile" instead of "child" and "puddin'" instead of "pudding," had once been a boarder in São José's School in Recife, a survival of the very time at which the story I had invented would have occurred? And here she was, telling me that not only did she exist but that her son José Maria existed too, and giving me to understand clearly enough that every bit of my supposed novel was actually true, while asking me to not to reveal the story but to suppress it out of respect for someone who, while she might be approaching the end of her existence, was still too much of a lady to have her life made public in such a manner— a fate, to her way of thinking, appropriate for actresses and comedians, but never for ladies.

I must admit that I was rendered practically speechless. It was most disconcerting. Someone should have been with me to share my perception of the very strange affair taking place in a house on the Square of São José do Ribamar. It was possible that the Dona Sinhá who confronted me might not be a psychiatric case after all, but—along with me—a metaphysical case.

It was Dona Sinhá who restored my calm. She was an authentic lady of the old school, very much a lady and very Brazilian—and there was nothing of the comedian about her, either in her sense of the word or in any other. She called for Amaro and the boy soon appeared, smiling his sweet smile. He had been cleaning the bird cages.

Dona Sinhá told the fellow, in the voice of a Wanderley and the daughter of plantation owners (she must surely be from Serinhaém, I thought), to bring us two cups of good, hot coffee. I took that as a sign that she was beginning to feel more kindly toward me, a good sign, after the lack of cordiality with which our conversation had begun. I was afraid of strong coffee, however, and asked that mine be brewed weak. She understood and told Amaro, still in an authoritative voice but with a very gentle expression in her eyes and on her face, to bring some port wine for me. In a low voice, almost a whisper, she murmured in the good Negro's ear: "From that bottle on top of the cupboard, where I keep the saints." Hearing this, I concluded that that must be the best port in the house, if it was stored in the same cupboard as the oratory. I felt more and more encouraged by her manner of welcoming me in that charmingly antiquated house. Not that it had the air of a museum, with the birds singing and a Negro boy whistling popular tunes of the day as he cleaned the cages. To tell the truth, however, I would have preferred for Dona Sinhá to send for a soothing drink of maracujá.[6] For all that these small signs of old-fashioned Brazilian hospitality had reconciled me to Dona Sinhá, I still felt bewildered at what was happening.

This was hardly surprising. I was becoming involved in something uncanny in that house in São José do Ribamar.

---

[6] Passion-flower fruit, the juice of which is drunk for its refreshing taste and calming effect.

When Dona Sinhá offered me the goblet of port wine, I suspect that my hands were shaking as much as those of the old lady—hers from advanced age, and mine from nervous excitement. For what was happening to me was a unique and unexpected adventure. Where and to whom had the same thing, or anything like it, ever happened before? In my English books on facts that modern research calls parapsychic or supranormal phenomena, I had never run across an account of any such phenomenon as this: a real Dona Sinhá proving to be the same person I had conceived for my novel—the very same, in personality and even in looks, that I had imagined. With the same religious son; the same origin—daughter of a sugar-plantation owner; the same house in São José; the same love affair, perhaps, with "the Frenchman."

I took another look at José Maria's portrait with its great seraphic eyes, decked out like the image of a saint. Dona Sinhá only exclaimed, in a voice that no longer held the authoritative accents of her commands to Amaro but was now almost mellifluously sad: "My little saint!" The old paintings were portraits of Dona Sinhá's father and mother, who had been the owners of the Olindeta Plantation until they died. I imagined her fastidious blond mother to have been, if not a Wanderley, then an Acioly Lins or a Cavalcanti. This prompted me to ask whether she was a Wanderley, as in my novelist's conception of her background. Dona Sinhá confirmed my guess: yes, her mother had been a Rocha Wanderley.

"Well, then," I exclaimed, beginning to be more reconciled to the mystery that was developing, "we are relatives." She smiled, still more inclined to like the intruder who had come to announce his intention of writing a novel about "Dona Sinhá and her son the priest," the publication of which her aristocratic modesty impelled her to try to stop if she could.

At this point I was sufficiently encouraged to say to her: "Dona Sinhá, please let me write my novel. I'll show the whole book to you before it is published, and if you agree, I'll come once a week to hear José Maria's story from you. The book will be a story about José Maria, but without you there wouldn't have been a José Maria. I'll have to tell a little about you too."

Dona Sinhá hesitated but finally agreed. It was arranged that I would come back the following Thursday with my notebook and pencil. She would tell me about her little angel, and I would write the biography of an unknown saint.

What filled my thoughts was the desire to compare my "Dona Sinhá," my "son the priest," my "Frenchman," with Dona Sinhá, the priest, and the Frenchman of whom the old lady who lived in the Square of São José do Ribamar had promised to speak. The fact was that I was plunged to my very soul into a possibly unique psychic adventure —one that was worthy of a communication to the London psychologists and the Duke University scientists who were engaged in investigating just such supranormal phenomena.

In my first attempt at fiction, I had tried to invent

something, but what I thought I had invented had turned out to be fact. To what extent would reality confirm my supposed invention? That was what my interviews with the elderly lady, my distant relative, would reveal. It was the death of a novel, but the birth of a mystery deserving the attention of the metapsychologists.

2

I LEFT Dona Sinhá's house as though returning from a kind of spiritualist séance—not religious spiritualism, but the other kind.

What had happened to me was certainly fantastic enough, although no phantoms were involved—no chairs propelling themselves from one corner of the room to another; no little red-haired English Katies, long years dead, materializing before the eyes of expert laboratory physicists.

Dona Sinhá had warned me, when accompanying me to the door after inquiring about my family and wanting to know a little about my private life (whether I was married; whether I frequented cafés; the names of my parents; whether I had any brothers or sisters), always to come alone and not to tell anyone about our meetings. It was as though she were signing a secret pact with me, a pact of silence concerning everything that she was about to tell me about her son—a saint, in her eyes—who had died so long before.

I was not to let anyone know what was happening in São José do Ribamar. Not that it was a love affair to conceal from my family, as any normally discreet Don Juan would to conform with our present-day, though al-

ready decrepit, bourgeois civilization. It was, nevertheless, such a strange adventure that I decided—as I wandered slowly through the old familiar streets of São José
as though in need of them and of the soothing shadows of
those narrow, friendly streets to reassure me that I had
not gone raving mad—that it must be carried on in secrecy, in secrecy and silence. Not even my closest friend
would share this secret of mine. I resolved not to let even
my father and mother know of my meetings with Dona
Sinhá, the elderly lady whose white hands were already a
little tremulous, and whose dragging steps contrasted
sharply with her still-strong voice and dancing eyes. It
was just as though I were concealing a love affair with
some artful, piquantly experienced Frenchwoman or
fiery mulatto girl. The day would surely come when I
could reveal my strange adventure to those around me
without running the risk of nipping it in the bud with my
indiscretion.

That there should be a real Dona Sinhá, the mother of
a priest and a rather anachronistic old lady who, on hearing of a novel about a mother and her priest son should
imagine herself to have been exposed by a brash author,
was not to be wondered at, I pondered as I approached
Penha Square. Even today Brazil is full of elderly ladies
whose families call them "Sinhá." A good many of them
probably have sons who are priests, and make fritters at
Carnival time and canjica [1] on Saint John's Eve—good,

[1] A dish made from corn mush, sugar, cinnamon, and coconut
milk.

typically Brazilian mothers of priests, who live with their sons, completing their apostleship throughout the interior of our vast Brazil.

But the story was more complex than that. I had been summoned by a real Dona Sinhá of flesh and blood who corresponded so closely to the image of my fictitious Dona Sinhá, in physical appearance as well as in background, that the coincidence seemed to take on all the characteristics of a paranormal phenomenon. I had not, it is true, decided on a name for Dona Sinhá's son; but I had thought of calling him, if not José Maria, then at least some similar name. It was simply amazing. And there was Dona Sinhá's background: she came from a family of plantation owners. There was the fact that she was a Wanderley, just as I had imagined my Dona Sinhá to be—a fair, aristocratic Wanderley who still possessed in her old age the good manners taught her by French nuns—the Dorotheans, perhaps. The Dona Sinhá whom I had just met seemed to have all of the characteristics of the fictitious one.

And then there was "the Frenchman." I had thought that "the Frenchman," at least, was purely my own invention—although based, of course, on the fact that many young Brazilians in the days of Dona Sinhá's youth had, like a brother of Cardinal Joaquim Arcoverde with whom I had been acquainted, completed their studies in Belgium or in France. But for just such a Frenchman or Belgian to have a part in the life of the real Dona Sinhá was too much of a coincidence not to be mysterious; or rather, it was a challenge to those who see in coincidences of the type studied by Jung nothing more than problems which human reason is capable of illuminating. I am not such a rationalist as to go to that extreme; but I *am* analytical, and that cluster of coincidences cried out for analysis. As for having heard from someone else the story of the real Dona Sinhá with whom I had just spoken, I was perfectly sure I had not. My story, my novel, my Dona Sinhá had been invented by me, in the same way that any author invents stories and characters for a work of fiction. How did it happen, then, that my Dona Sinhá and the real one were alike in so many ways?

I was still thinking about it as I stopped at Dudu's door in Penha Square. *Dudu was the owner of a restaurant whose popularity was never to be equaled, after his death, by any other in Recife. After he was gone, no one would ever again serve such perfectly salted sarapatel,*[2] *such well-seasoned fish, or a feijoada* [3] *so Brazilian in the taste of its jerked beef and so tropical in the ardor of its burning hot pepper sauce as the sarapatel, the fish, and the feijoada that plump Dudu in his jersey, already getting along in years, prepared for me and my friends.* The only thing I could do now, I realized as I hesitated at Dudu's door, was to keep my analytical wits about me in the face of the Dona Sinhá mystery. I should have to call

[2] Brazilian haggis, a typical dish of Recife.
[3] Brazil's national dish: black beans cooked with pork, jerked beef, tripe, and sausage, served with rice, kale, and manioc meal.

upon all the phlegmatic steadiness I had acquired in my scientific studies. Now it remained for me to determine, in my future conversations with Dona Sinhá, how far these abnormal coincidences persisted: between her and the character (in the English sense of the word "character") that I had invented, and her own life and the life I had imagined this fictional character to have lived. Then there was the question of her relations with her son the priest, her father, her husband, and "the Frenchman."

Instead of opening the door to Dudu's restaurant, I entered the Church of the Penha.

Penha Church does not arouse any enthusiasm in me today, and in fact never did at any time, but I can not help admiring what there is of art inside it (the outside is more than a little banal). It is monk's art, of course—the art of an Italian cast adrift in a Brazil that was still exotic to him—but Christian, at least: Christianized, Latinized, Romanized by the Portuguese.

The familiar churchly hush did me good; it calmed and soothed me. I wondered what sort of relationship the real Dona Sinhá had had with the church of the Capuchins in her youth. Had José Maria been baptized in this old church by some blond-bearded friar? Had he made his First Communion with the monks? I resolved to talk to other old São José inhabitants who might have known José Maria.

None of this had been a part of my original outline for *Mother and Son*, but it was the sort of material that lent itself to speculation. Perhaps it would be interesting to include in the course of the novel a few such details, now that I had a real, living, knowledgeable Dona Sinhá to supply me with precise particulars which would be exact —historically exact—instead of fictitious.

All of this was humiliating, I thought as I sat in the church, for someone who had wanted to free himself, though Dona Sinhá and her priest son, from History's domination of literature as well as of science. It was as though History had surprised me in the act of deceiving her by flirting with Fiction, and before the act of treachery could be consummated, had brought me back to her feminine but strong, enveloping, imperious arms. I had tasted the honey of deceit, nonetheless, and History was not to think that my flirtation with Fiction was altogether Platonic. There was a dash of sensuality in it. I *had* invented Dona Sinhá and her son. If History chose to present me with a Dona Sinhá and a José Maria exactly like mine, I was sure I had preceded her with my own little invention. Perhaps no one would believe it, but for me it was enough to have had the exquisite experience of creating a plot and characters, if not out of thin air, then for the most part, at least, out of my own imagination. If History, asserting herself as absolute mistress of my poor scribblings, would not let me betray her in public even once, then I should have to resign myself and be patient.

However, it was still too soon to jump to conclusions. The adventure into which I had plunged might lead me to such novel discoveries about the relationship between historical time and artistic, fictitious time that all of my present thinking would have to be revised. Could it be that there was an artistically fictitious time which was pursued and captured by historical time so that the two sometimes merged into one? Was there an apparently artificial truth—that of fiction—seemingly independent of history but in fact historically true, which, floating in the psychic atmosphere, might be caught, through some still unknown metaphysical process, by the sensitive imagination of some writer more than usually intent on his search for a theme and characters? I thought of all this in Penha Church, without really seeing what I stared at, including the rather fine engraving of Dom Vital:[4] a Dom Vital who was, if anything, too faithful to the original—virile, proud, and healthy—to correspond to the classic Brazilian conception of a saint—the kind of individual whom the majority would tend to regard as a saint —almost always a suffering martyr, sickly, weak, and wan, *like Dom Vital as a child;* but cunning, more through intuition than as a result of any wisdom learned in school, in his struggles with the World and the Devil. *In Penha itself there was, I noticed, a cult of devotion to St. Felix, a Capuchin lay brother who might be described as a weak and wan Italian—a little hillbilly lay brother of the Capuchins, a country bumpkin dressed up in a Fran-*

---

[4] Vital Maria Gonçalves de Oliveira (1844–78), Bishop of Olinda and Recife, condemned to prison for his unrelenting struggle for the rights of the Church as against those of the Imperial State during the reign of Dom Pedro II.

ciscan's habit, but wily in his dealings with Satan.

Dona Sinhá had longed for her son to achieve saint-
hood. The real Dona Sinhá, imitating even in this the character I had invented, adorned the boy's portrait as though
it were a picture of St. Louis Gonzaga. José Maria had not
been at all bad-looking. Judging by the photograph, he
had taken after his father rather than his mother, although
he did have a certain resemblance to her and the Wanderleys. He was slender, refined, and pale, with dark hair
and delicate features which made him look more like a
girl than a boy. There was something almost angelic
about him which was hard to interpret in purely biologi-
cal terms. Once again, I feel obliged to point out that this
was "my" Dona Sinhá's son before he appeared in the
photograph I had seen in the house in São José do Ribamar, adorned with flowers: the boyish priest who had
died before he could be ordained, looking more like a girl
than a young man in his expression, made angelic by his
intense and sincere religious life. If he had been set adrift
into the life of the world, he might have turned into a
mollycoddle with a mellifluous voice and mincing ways,
making eyes at the husky boys with a desire like that of a
lustful woman for any ostensibly masculine male. As it
was, Jesus Christ had become for him the only God and
Man. The Church has won many such victories over Nature.

In this very church—which I had visited frequently in
the old days, sometimes going there to drink beer served
warm on a rough-hewn Tuscan table with the friars who

were my friends—I had once met such a priest, with a big, man-hungry eyes of a woman, who gazed covetously at every real man who entered the church. He had, nevertheless, been devoted to Christ and to the saints. The conflict between his religious vocation and his longing for sexual adventures that were out of the question for a monk was his constant torment. I was acquainted with another friar who even smelled like a saint, I thought, and who was a true saint in his life. Extraordinary goodness emanated from his presence wherever he went. *He was an Italian, and his name was Friar Daniel. I do not remember ever having seen on the face of man or woman, old man or child, a smile like Friar Daniel's. St. Francis of Assisi might have smiled in just such a way.*

There was, however, an anti-Friar Daniel in the Penha Church in my boyhood days when I was friendly with some of the monks, although not religious enough to go to mass and pray to the saints, and certainly having no vocation for the Church. This anti-Friar Daniel was like the depraved monks caricatured in books. One day, entering the sacristy in rubber-soled shoes (I had been playing tennis on the Anglican priest's court with some Englishmen from the Western Telegraph Company), what did my eyes behold but the lustful monk in his Capuchin robes, taking his pleasure à la française *with a little mulatto girl with her skirts pulled up, whom he had perched on a wide, innocent-looking jacarandá chest of drawers.*

The Church, I thought to myself, has always been able to weather this sort of thing. Some of its priests are less than priests, but to make up for the deficiency there are others who are more than priests. It was a pity that Dona Sinhá's son had not been one of their number. He might have become another Friar Daniel; but just before he could be ordained, he had died of a fever—typhoid, I believe; he had always been consumptive. (This detail —what illness had carried off Dona Sinhá's son—had not been included in my outline. I should have to try to find out from the admirably lucid old lady.)

Leaving the church, I went straight home. My one preoccupation was to keep my secret even from the family without looking too mysterious myself, or as though I were involved in a truly disconcerting mystery.

3

I MUST confess that when I returned home after that first encounter with Dona Sinhá, I told a lie. A small one, one of the so-called white lies—but still a lie. I was anxious to keep my colloquies with the old lady a secret.

My mother and sisters, with feminine curiosity, immediately wanted to know what "the woman who had written that note" had wanted with me. I told them that she was not a "woman" but a lady. A lady who had come down in the world, it was true, but a lady nevertheless. A noblewoman, in fact. She had been rich once; her people were plantation owners. It was impossible to imagine a Dona Sinhá who was not a lady, I added, with the intention of teaching my youngest sister something about semantics. By this time, mother and sisters had lost patience with my philological pedantry and verbal hair-splitting. One of them burst forth with the irritated question: "Well, then, what did the *lady* want?"

Exactly what I had thought at first when the note had been delivered, I replied. The little old lady—for she was a little old lady, at least eighty years old—had some family antiques to sell; and rather than see them in the hands of some bottle-and-rag man or on sale in an antique shop, she wanted them to go directly from her home to that of people for whom she had some esteem. The old lady must be having her difficulties, I went on sentimentally, hinting that I would like to help her, what with inflation (a puny sort of inflation we had in those days!), which affected some people more than others. That was the only reason she had been induced to part with her jacarandá furniture and her silver pitcher and basin. As a note of realism, I added that the pitcher and basin were exactly like ours—sheer invention, for the only article of silver I had seen in Dona Sinhá's house was a Portuguese tray of excellent quality. That was an unnecessary invention, I realized after I had said it. But one falsehood leads to another; and I was determined that not even my own family should learn about the adventure (an adventure for a snooper if not for a psychologist) into which I had been drawn in São José do Ribamar and which would lead me to I knew not what extremes. I was anxious to keep it a secret, because the slightest indiscretion might spoil it.

Who would ever have thought that for Dona Sinhá's sake I would take to stealing out of the house once a week without telling anyone where I was going, like the adolescent son of a stern father or an overprotective mother going through his first adventures with sex? Or that I would carefully avoid my friends, passing hurriedly by the doors of the pharmacies and cafés that I knew were the habitual haunts of friends and acquaintances? Yet that is the very procedure I followed after the day of my first meeting with Dona Sinhá. She had become for me a mystery which, if it were to continue, would have to be cultivated in secret.

I asked my elderly father, *a grandson of the plantation owner Manuel da Rocha Wanderley,* whether he knew anything about some Wanderleys who lived on a plantation called Olindeta. He told me he did, but had heard of them only vaguely. *In his childhood, Serinhaém, Rio Formoso, Água Preta, and Palmares were full of sugar plantations belonging to our Wanderley relatives, some of whom were Rocha Wanderleys, others Barros Wanderleys. There were so many, not all of them important, that it was hard to tell them apart except by the names of the plantations. Very few of the Wanderley plantation owners were, like Sebastião do Rosário, rich owners of splendid horses fitted out with equally splendid silver trappings. The plantations of the other Wanderleys were, with few exceptions, mediocre and run-of-the-mill— wretched little farms rather than plantations. Their owners were, more often than not, run-of-the-mill and mediocre themselves, with an occasional high-toned Pedro da Rocha Wanderley set apart from the fat, lazy Wanderleys, as slow-thinking as they were slow-talking, by his good breeding and quick, lively intelligence: the intelligence of a ruined hidalgo who consoled himself for having failed at growing sugar cane by speaking scornfully of others—especially of those successful planters who were neither fair-haired nor Wanderleys. To him they were nothing but so many vague Silvas whose grandfathers nobody had known, or else despised mulatto bastards. For until the end of the nineteenth century, the true Wanderleys of Pernambuco were almost invariably admirers of mulatto women and detractors of mulatto men—dyed-in-the-wool Aryans on the one hand and champions of miscegenation on the other.*

I realized that Dona Sinhá must come from a family of Wanderleys of this kind, blond as she was, with a complexion almost as fair as that of a European newly arrived in the tropics, and the whitest of hands. Only her speech was drawling and languid: tropicalized, Brazilianized; the speech of a delicate plantation lady who could be authoritative at times: "Do this, gal!" "Do that, boy!"

She would have to tell me a little about her father and mother and about Olindeta. There was no information about them in my outline. Not that such details were essential to my *Mother and Son,* but I might learn from Dona Sinhá, incidental to the main topic of our conversation, certain facts—historical facts—about Brazil's past.

For obviously I am virtually deformed as a professional sociologist by my preoccupation with history. Meditating on such concerns, I sometimes lost sight of the extraordinary fact that Dona Sinhá was a sort of copy of a character invented by me outside history, who had suddenly turned up as a historical original whom I in turn was to copy. If this process of original into copy was not a mystery, it was at least a series of coincidences, of the sort that are called "mere coincidences" in conventional language today. But the thought came to me again that for "mere coincidences" these were rather peculiar. It occurred to me once more that a Jung might have enjoyed studying them.

4

AND SO I began the lengthy process of gathering from Dona Sinhá the information that she brought to me from a time that had seemed dead and gone but was, in fact, alive with explanations of the present. While shaving one morning, taking my time as usual, I was interrupted by the voice—half censor, half guardian angel—which each of us hears inside him on occasion. This time it surprised me with a rather sharp admonition. "After all," said the voice, "what is it you intend to write? A novel? A historical narrative? An essay, like the essays by those Spanish authors you admire so much, beginning with Cervantes, who, even when they write novels for the general public, tuck essays inside the novels for a smaller but choicer coterie of readers?"

After such a warning, I was on the point of breaking off my conversations with Dona Sinhá and writing to my friends to beg them to stop announcing the publication of *Mother and Son*. I resolved to strangle mother and son in the manuscript and not to give them even the beginnings of life bestowed on many a character—without the public's ever making their acquaintance—on typewritten pages.

The truth was, however, that Dona Sinhá had become

irresistibly seductive to me. I was reminded of *Oswald de Andrade when he admitted to me that he was in love with a woman who was almost old enough to be his grandmother, and justified himself by repeating: "Freud would understand me; Freud would understand."* I thought of my own case as rather Freudian, although not so much so as Oswald's. My relationship with Dona Sinhá was simply one of empathy, directed toward the lady I had imagined rather than the real one.

After all, the plot of the novel that I had woven around an abstract Dona Sinhá, her priest son, and a certain "Frenchman"—a sentimental triangle which I had discovered, thanks to the fact that Dona Sinhá of São José do Ribamar, Recife, had come to exist in actual time and space—had something Freudian about it. In order to understand it I would have to let myself be caught up in the romance. It was not to be wondered at that the author should, in this case, suffer the influence of his own characters and be attracted by the maternal charm of Dona Sinhá, thus following the example of "the Frenchman" or the priest son himself. But let us not get ahead of our story by speculating about the triangle and its ramifications.

At this point it is essential that the reader be at least superficially informed as to how her son came to occupy such a predominant place in Dona Sinhá's life, and why he continued to absorb her thoughts even after his death. The very same thing had happened to the boy: he had grown up feeling such an exclusive love for his mother

31

that the only reason he wanted to be a priest—or so he confessed on one occasion to his best friend—was that the cult of Our Lady was part of the Catholic religion. One might add, thinking of Freud's discoveries, that Our Lady had become identified in his mind with the person of his own mother, with Dona Sinhá. I reached this conclusion after listening to Dona Sinhá and other elderly persons. In a way, I was gathering material for a biography rather than trying to write a novel.

Readers unsympathetic to Catholicism and its Our Lady, or rather its many and various Our Ladies, are likely to consider the story of Dona Sinhá's son absurd. For the Our Lady of José Maria's devotion was not an abstract Mother of Jesus and Mother of Men. She was a very special Our Lady: Our Lady of Sorrows, whose grief brought her tenderly close to José Maria's own sorrows as a child who was tormented, humiliated, and ridiculed by the other children and even by adults, who shouted at him in the streets of São José on his way home from school: "Here comes Missy! Here comes Missy!" That was what they shouted in the street. At school it was even worse.

Why Missy? Because Dona Sinhá, a widow alone in Recife, far from her plantation relatives in Serinhaém and Rio Formoso, had brought up her only son in her own image. Her husband had not made a strong enough impression on her for his memory to have become a sentimental cult to add to the religious and social rite that widowhood had become for her. Dona Sinhá was a liturgical widow from the day of her husband's death. She was always dressed in black, or in purple as a daring concession. She did not indulge in low necklines; nor much lace; nor perfume; nor gewgaws; nor any thoughts of a second marriage. She was obsessed by the idea of living for her son and for him alone, for her only child. Yes, she would live only for her son, she thought. So the neighbors recognized and the family proclaimed, letting it be known that she was not only a mother to José Maria but grandmother and nursemaid as well. She did not like anyone to touch her little naked baby or change his diapers, not even black Inácia, who had come with her from the plantation as a wedding present from her father and in whom she trusted absolutely. The other Negro women had to admire the little white master, the pure little darling, from a distance. He was as pure as a Baby Jesus lying in a manger. So fine, with hair almost as light as his mother's. Even his little penis was just the kind a Baby Jesus would have. Sinhá would gaze at him as though he really were a Baby Jesus. She treated him as though he were one. And as the little boy grew, she covered him with blue ribbons as though he had been a real live Baby Jesus, and let his hair grow long like the hair of angels and little girls. When José Maria came down with an attack of diarrhea that was not at all angelic, and Sinhá had to call the doctor, buy medicine with French names, and let Inácia help her change the bedclothes—on a bed that was always kept white, pure, and immaculate, with its linens edged in lace and trimmed with blue ribbon, as though it were a horizontal altar on which the saint could take his rest after the manner of ordinary tired mortals—she ordered that a novena be said in the house. Father Zacarias was called in; quantities of candles were lighted; prayers were sung as though it had been a night in May, the month of Mary; and the sorely afflicted Sinhá, clinging to the Lady of Sorrows, promised the saint that if her child survived his diarrhea—probably a treacherous touch of colic, which the doctor in his black frockcoat and the medicines with French names seemed powerless to cure —then he would be a priest, a servant of Our Lady of Sorrows.

José Maria survived. His illness left him very weak and very pale. His eyes seemed to become sadder, more lackluster than those of other children. For some time he could hardly see at all. But his little hands grew more restless, more sensitive, more inquisitive than anyone else's, as though he could see more through his fingertips than through his eyes. It was almost as if he were blind; as if he sensed the world—the people he touched; the cats he petted; the birds he took out of their cages so that he could feed them himself from one cupped hand while holding them—warm, eager, and quivering—in the other; his mother's soft arm, to which he loved to cling as he fell asleep; the purple plush collars on Dona Sinhá's dresses which he liked to stroke—in a way that was uniquely his own. And so José Maria grew up in São José do Ribamar, a singular boy, different from other children, a sort of blind-man's guide to himself.

Every so often Inácia would take him to the courtyard of the church to play with the other little boys. But it was no use; the children saw in Dona Sinhá's son a playmate who was not like them. If his presence did not annoy them, neither did they particularly welcome it. José Maria, for his part, hardly felt strong enough to take part in the games the boys in the churchyard played. He would ask Inácia to take him out of the yard, and they would walk as far as the edge of the water, which strongly attracted him. He loved any contact with the water—almost pure ocean water—that lapped São José; the cold water, and especially the warm, heated by the sun, that was like the water that Inácia heated in the kitchen kettle for his bath in the wooden tub. He feared the deep water, but mingled with his fear was a vague desire to descend into its mystery—protected, of course, by Iemanjá.

For Inácia often spoke to him of Iemanjá, the Lady of the Waters.[1] Dona Sinhá, orthodox and a little French in her Catholicism as a former pupil of the nuns of São José (*those Dorothean nuns of São José, the protegées of Dom Vital, with one of whom, Mother Virgínia, he was said by evil gossips to be in love*), never missed a chance to remind him that those stories about Iemanjá were nigger talk. Inácia was a fine person, who had been brought up on the plantation as though she were the master's own

---

[1] The sea goddess Iemanjá, or Janaína, holds in the Afro-Brazilian religious cults a revered place corresponding to that of the Mother of God in Catholicism.

adopted daughter, but she was a Negro all the same. Her mother had been a slave straight from Africa who had spoken nothing but nagô [2] and had had a hard time learning to pray in Portuguese. José Maria was not to believe any of that nigger talk. All that business about Iemanjá was just a story the Negroes had made up. There was only one Lady of the waters, the dry land, men, beasts, even snakes, and she was the Mother of Jesus and Mother to all who followed Jesus and honored His holy Mother.

The first time a Ribamar fisherman presented him with a little fish, still alive and struggling to get back into the water, José Maria grasped it eagerly, shouting that the fishy belonged to him and nobody else. He carried it home, very proud of himself; and after that he started raising fishes in a glass vase that Dona Sinhá gave him, a mock aquarium.

Even more than the caged birds in the house, the fish in his aquarium became, aside from the caresses his mother gave him and those he gave his mother, the greatest pleasure of José Maria's childhood. Dona Sinhá seemed happy to think that they were her only rivals for her son's affection, although of course she never neglected her efforts to increase his devotion to Our Lady— and to the good Lord Jesus and the saints too, naturally; but to Our Lady above all. The image of Our Lady was on the medal of finest gold that hung around José Maria's neck, and his fingers caressed it with the tenderness of one who sensed the presence of a holy celestial Mother in

[2] The language of the Yoruba tribe.

that gold—his other mother. Or perhaps she was the same person. Perhaps the two mothers were one and the same.

When José Maria turned six, Dona Sinhá felt that it was time to start teaching him to read and write. She took charge of this duty herself—not an easy one, for the boy was still a convalescent. He was still thin and frail and ate very little. "Picky," Inácia called him. She sometimes gave him cakes which she patted into balls out of manioc mush, rude, plebeian food, which José Maria ate with a fairly good appetite, as though he enjoyed a holiday from the aristocratic gruel and porridge prepared for him by Dona Sinhá from the finest flour sold at the grocery stores on the Rua Nova.

José Maria was not as interested in the primer, the copybook, or the multiplication tables as he was in the birds he still cared for with his own hands or the Ribamar fishes, which he still raised lovingly in his little aquarium, picking them up, patting them, and even squeezing them almost with cruelty at times, only to let them escape from his momentarily cruel fingers back to the comforting maternal water to recover after their adventures.

Even so, the boy slowly learned to spell, to count, to read, to write, and to scrawl pictures with colored pencils. But Dona Sinhá made sure that he did not work too hard over any of these exercises. She warned her son not to tire himself out but to rest from the dry, uninteresting lessons by playing with the birds or with the fish in his aquarium, and she sent him out for walks in the Ribamar courtyard or along its paved streets, with Inácia holding his hand. Sometimes José Maria was taken to the priest's house—so that he would become accustomed to a priest's life, his mother said—where he was invariably given a little medal or a holy picture.

At the priest's house every Sunday there were orthodox fritters—the kind that is always served in priests' houses —fried by an old Negro woman of whom José Maria grew as fond as he was of the fritters. Fluffy and light, they were just like the fritters Dona Sinhá sometimes made for him, and they turned to manna in the little boy's mouth. The manna that Our Lord sent down to His people must have tasted just like those fritters, thought José Maria, who was learning Bible stories from his mother.

José Maria found the father good company too, all the more so as he already loved to hear mass and follow the gestures of the priest in his snow-white lace and vestments whose greens, purples, and bright yellows began to mean something to the child, to whom Dona Sinhá explained everything that was holy or had to do with churches and religious processions.

José Maria had already gone with her to the Penha Church, which was being rebuilt at that time and was full of scaffolding. He had visited the altars of the brand-new saints one by one and had run his hand down the massive columns of Italian marble, still new and smoother than anything else in the world. The friars raised the gooseflesh on him at first. It was not so much their beards that frightened him as the terrible solemnity

38

of their countenances, their gestures, and their voices as missionary preachers of the Holy Word. Even though he did not as yet know the meaning of sin, he clung to his mother in fear, a fear that was partly Inácia's. She was terrified of the cords with which the Capuchins whipped people who were possessed by devils. But Dona Sinhá called the good friars by name: "This is Brother So-and-So, dear. This is Brother Such-and-Such. Ask for his blessing." When he heard their sonorous, sweet-sounding names and saw the smiles of the friars who were friends of Dona Sinhá, the little boy's fear of those gruff-looking Italians was assuaged. He would go back home, impatient to tell people that he had been with the friars, had been given their blessing, and had even pulled on the cords of the custodian's St. Francis habit, and that the friar had smiled at him just as he smiled at Dona Sinhá, saying: "That's for little boys who don't obey their mothers." He was in no danger of being punished for disobedience. Even when his mother gave him nasty medicine and covered his nose herself so he wouldn't notice its sticky-sweet smell, didn't he take it like a good boy?

5

BUT was José Maria really free from sin? Was he an angel who had never sinned? Dona Sinhá would have been ready to swear that he was. But he, José Maria, had already begun to think of himself as a sinner. For the truth was that for some time now, whenever he was alone in his warm bath, he had taken to playing with his penis, patting it as though it were a baby bird or squeezing it as though it were one of the little fish in his aquarium. From the patting and squeezing came pleasant sensations which he did not dare mention to his mother, nor to Inácia, nor to anyone else. It was his secret. Just as it was a secret that he had brought home from the priest's house and hidden among his toys a card all covered with gold which he thought was ever so pretty. It had probably been thrown away by the reverend father's old Negro housekeeper; but neither she nor the priest nor anyone else had given it to him. He had taken possession of that card, which, it was true, no one else had wanted, but which had not actually been given to him. His acquisition had caused him so much uneasiness that he had hidden the card away without showing it to anyone. He kept it a secret, just as he kept secret that other adventure which he repeated over and over in his warm bath in the wooden tub which had been brought from his grandfather's plantation especially for him.

He was surely a sinner. There was no doubt in his mind that he had committed his first two sins. To think that he, who had been dedicated to Our Lady of Sorrows and was being educated for the priesthood, should be guilty of such sins against his Mother in Heaven and against Jesus too, the perfect Son of God and Mary!

He began to feel that his hands were betraying him. It was through his hands that he had begun to do wrong. What filthy hands he had, unworthy of the rest of his body. Unworthy to caress his mother, to gather flowers for Our Lady, to make the sign of the cross. No one knew about it, not even his mother. But that other Mother knew. It was from her that José Maria felt he ought to beg forgiveness, and by her hand that he must be punished—how, he had no idea. Maybe she would tear off his hands. Never again would he pet his little animals, nor stroke Dona Sinhá's soft arm, nor her plushes, nor her velvets, nor Mister Cat's fur. Never again would he eat manioc mush and giblets with his hands, feeling the food between his fingers and enjoying its flavor not only with his palate and his eyes but also with his fingertips, feeling it with his whole hand, smearing all over himself the goodies that his mother or Inácia made for him, without bothering to use a fork or a silver spoon and without giving a thought to his table manners. It would be a terrible misfortune to be a little boy without hands. Maybe it would be even worse than being blind. It would certainly

be worse than being deaf and dumb, even though he felt
frightened when he thought of Ezequiel, the deaf-mute
who had lived for several years in the churchyard of São
José do Ribamar. The fishermen said that Our Lady had
torn out his tongue and stopped up his ears because he
had been born under an unlucky star, accursed in the
eyes of Mary and those of his own mother. What if he,
José Maria, had been born unlucky too, born to bring
sorrow to Our Lady and to his mother? What if his hands
were the perdition of his body and his soul? Once José
Maria had heard one of the Penha friars read from the
Bible about such things. The part of a man that offended
him should be cut off. And an altar boy in Father Zacarias's house had told him that hair would grow on the
hand of a child who sinned against the commandments
of Holy Mother Church, just as if the hand had turned
into an animal's paw. He was using his hands for wrong-
doing. He had stolen that card from the priest—that is,
not stolen it, exactly, but taken it home without asking
anyone's permission; he had not asked its owner or the
priest's old housekeeper whether he could have it. Taking
the card had been such a bad thing to do that he had
hidden it among his toys.

And what about the way he played with his own penis?
His fingertips itched with the desire to touch his "pretty,"
as Inácia called it, as soon as his mother put him to bed
at night after they had said their prayers together. It was
as though the little penis burned with longing to be
touched by his small devil's fingers. Such caresses were

42

not forbidden by the Ten Commandments, but they must be wrong. Something told him that they were. The very fact that he concealed them from his mother, just as he had concealed the card he had brought home from the priest's house, was proof enough that they were a sin—a sin committed with his hands, in secret, alone, in the dark.

José Maria took to praying with all his might to Our Lady of Sorrows to keep him from being tempted by that strange pleasure, which no one had taught him, but in which he indulged through the spontaneous art of his own fingers, and which was certainly a sin. He might have learned something about it from the altar boys he met at the priest's house, which he frequented more often now that Dona Sinhá had entrusted the religious instruction of her son to the reverend father. But the altar boys did not inspire him with enough confidence to make him want to talk to them about such an intimate matter. They were big, half-grown boys, and there was nothing at all seraphic about them. One of them was a gangling country lad who reminded José Maria of a saci [1] and who actually smoked the priest's cornsilk cigarettes when no one was looking. Even while they were serving mass, the gangling boy and his companion sometimes snickered in a scandalous way, no doubt remembering the wicked things they talked about in the parish priest's yard or

---

[1] In Brazilian folklore, a one-legged, pipe-smoking, mischievous Negro imp who sets snares for travelers and plays pranks on the unsuspecting.

thinking up tricks to play on the devout. Even the poor pious old women were not safe from their teasing: the boys would tie paper tails onto their black skirts or steal their pocket handkerchiefs. One of them had told another that José Maria was such an innocent that his name ought to be Maria José. It was a wonder they didn't call him Missy!

No: it was impossible for José Maria to discuss confidential matters with the altar boys, or the children who played in the churchyard in Ribamar, or his mother, or the priest. He might tell Inácia, though. Maybe one day he would ask her what kind of pleasure it was that his "pretty" gave him when he touched it with his fingers. Or was it possible that Inácia suspected his sin? Had she already guessed his secret?

His mother was life itself to him, but on the other hand he could hardly imagine living without Inácia. Walking hand in hand with Inácia and guided by her faulty Portuguese—"This-a-way, chile! Up heah, honey!"—he had discovered the seashore, the river, the fish, and the Iemanjá whose existence his mother denied—"Nigger talk!"—but Inácia confirmed: "They *is* a Iemanjá, chile! White folks say they ain't, but they is, I even seed her, yessuh!"

Many of the words that José Maria used he had learned from the Negro woman. Sometimes Dona Sinhá was scandalized: "Honey, who taught you to say that?" It was always Inácia. Inácia had taught him to say "chicken ass." Inácia had taught him to say "big-mouth" instead of "gos-

sip," "tote" instead of "carry," "high-tail it" instead of
"run." And then there were all the nice juicy words like
cangapé,[2] mamparreiro,[3] cafunje.[4] It annoyed Dona
Sinhá to surprise in the vocabulary of her son, as tenderly
raised as though he had been a little girl, brought up to be
a priest or even a saint, those unworthy accretions from
plebeian mouths. Some of those words came straight
from Africa. She forbade José Maria to repeat them and
scolded Inácia for having a dirty mouth. But in this she
was unjust to the Negress. Without actually being impudent, Inácia answered her back rather sharply that those
were the only words she knew. If Dona Sinhá thought the
way she talked was so ugly, she could sew up her mouth
like a toad's. Dona Sinhá had to give in and laugh at the
Negro woman, saying in her slightly whining Wanderley
voice: "That's just what I ought to do! You sure do have a
toad's mouth. More like a toad's mouth than a person's,
you sassy nigger. All you're good for is to be a slave back
on the plantation!" And both women laughed. But José
Maria was sometimes disconcerted by these exchanges between his mother and Inácia, between the white woman
and the black one. Sometimes he was overwhelmed by
such a strong desire to see Africa and Inácia's people and
the waters of Iemanjá that in the longing he sensed a be-
trayal of his mother.

Perhaps his sin of playing with the "pretty" had some-

---

[2] A swift, unexpected kick in the calf of the leg.
[3] Dawdler, procrastinator.
[4] Rascal.

thing African about it, something of witchcraft, voodoo, black magic. Perhaps Inácia would be able to throw some light on a subject about which he was so much in the dark—Inácia, who looked at him sometimes with eyes that seemed to guess his deepest thoughts more easily than Dona Sinhá herself.

And yet, how could he talk to Inácia about such a thing? Inácia—since she was a grown woman and he was beginning to be a man—was not permitted by Dona Sinhá to see him without his clothes on. She was a stranger now to his body, which was becoming more like a man's body and less like that of a child. No one ever saw him naked any more; he was the only one who saw himself from head to foot—he and the big mirror in the front room where Dona Sinhá dressed and put on her corset. Inácia was expert at pulling the laces tight, a scene at which José Maria was no longer allowed to be present. He was beginning to be a man now, and a man destined for the priesthood at that.

José Maria kept his sin to himself—the sin of a boy who was no longer innocent but still inexperienced; a boy who felt Inácia's plump breasts with the tips of his fingers when he hugged her. Inácia would draw back as though affronted, or as though he had touched something sacred: "Don' you mess around there, Zemaria. You pretty near a man, an' a man what's goin' to be a priest!"

Soon it would be time for his First Communion. He would have to confess; and then the priest would learn, to José Maria's shame and that of his mother, that Dona Sinhá's angelic child, dedicated by his mother to the Virgin as a future priest from the day he was born, was not the little innocent he had looked but a small boy who was already a sinner. He was worse than the altar boys who mouthed obscenities in the priest's yard, tormented the pious old women, smoked cornsilk cigarettes stolen from the reverend father, but who when they were alone did not (or so he imagined) do what he, José Maria, did.

What was the secret of that pleasure, which something warned him was an ugly sin, perhaps even a mortal one? José Maria dreamed of discovering what it was. If he could have, he would have taken apart the very instrument of pleasure, the little doll of flesh that was alive. He had once taken apart a puppet dressed in silk which squeaked and moved its arms and legs when the child squeezed it with his fingers, rumpling its red and yellow silk. He had taken other toys to pieces too. He had broken in half a harmonica that was almost exactly like the one that belonged to a real musician, the strapping, prancing mulatto who played in the Army band and sometimes came to visit his father, a fisherman in Ribamar. Someone had given José Maria the toy harmonica for a present on his fifth birthday, and for a long time it was kept in Dona Sinhá's big dresser drawer, wrapped in a velvet cloth. That harmonica had given him extraordinary pleasure for more than a year. Beautiful, clear sounds came out when the little boy blew on it. It was so new and pretty that it gleamed in his hands. The children in the courtyard were consumed with envy when José Maria

47

went out walking with his harmonica, holding Inácia by the hand. But as soon as the music that came out of the harmonica began to sound harsh and scratchy instead of clear and beautiful, José Maria seized on that for an excuse to see what his beloved but mysterious plaything looked like inside. He loved the harmonica. But something that was stronger than his love for the instrument filled him with a strange longing to which he at last succumbed one day, out of the sight of Dona Sinhá and Inácia, to take the harmonica to pieces and lay bare its secret mystery. It was a most exciting adventure to the child, who had sometimes envied the altar boys their even more daring adventures, such as cutting open lizards with a penknife to see their insides, still warm with life. What was his "pretty" like inside?

6

JOSÉ MARIA, already a full-fledged sinner who had made his first confessions, been forgiven his first sins, and been forewarned against some of the lesser as well as the greater enemies of the soul, no longer studied only religion with the priest, but Latin as well.

New forms, new colors, new sounds reached his ears and eyes through the Latin phrases and illustrations in his books, reinforcing the words and manners he had learned from Dona Sinhá and separating him from Inácia and the other Negroes, the street urchins, and the Ribamar fishermen, with their varied corruptions of spoken Portuguese, which were sometimes too full of African words and sometimes too sweet: baby talk, slave talk, with no *r*'s, *s*'s, or *l*'s.

Not that José Maria divorced himself completely from that soft, viscous, humid, deliciously sticky, fraternal, even servile world, which was at the same time, he thought, mysteriously superior in many ways and which had become a refuge against certain rather dry, dictatorial demands imposed on her beloved son by Dona Sinhá. It was a refuge, too, against the blacks and purples of the black-and-purple-garbed widow, who dressed in gray only on rare occasions, eschewing any color or gaiety in her garments and making her son's clothes in obedience to the same mournful pattern as her own. Dona Sinhá preferred chicken-and-rice soup, which reminded José Maria of the time when he had been sick, served with a sparkling-clean silver spoon, to crab claw, which Inácia had taught José Maria to eat with his fingers. Then, too, Sinhá did not want to hear about—or let her son hear about—Iemanjá and the tales of sea goddesses that Fisherman Tonho enjoyed telling the younger fishermen as they sat in front of the Church of São José do Ribamar on moonlit nights. The only Mother whose influence over José Maria Dona Sinhá would admit as being greater than her own, the only other woman who could occupy his thoughts, was the Virgin Mary, Mother of Jesus— Mother of the Christ Child.

In Iemanjá, the Mother of Waters, Dona Sinhá recognized a rival, a mystical rival only, but nonetheless a rival to herself and even to the Virgin. Dona Sinhá may have sensed that her son was in danger of being seduced by the siren whom the fishermen of São José do Ribamar worshipped almost as devoutly as they did the Mother of God. She did not like the sea. Once she said to me, giving expression to her pride in being white, that she could never trust mulatto women with green eyes. Green, she went on, was the color of the waves, which everyone knew were treacherous. She forgot that the waves could also be blue, and that the eyes of her Wanderley ancestors —whom she considered perfectly honest men, though hardly saints—had been blue.

João Gaspar, a brother of Dona Sinhá whom I met in her house one day, told me that Dona Sinhá would not leave her son alone with the fishermen, who were, she knew, devotees of Iemanjá, or with João Gaspar himself, for fear that he would lead the boy to the charms of other sirens who were less watery and more earthy, less fishy and more female. He had always respected the childlike innocence of his nephew José Maria, but when the child began to grow up, he thought it his duty as an uncle to oppose Sinhá's absolute dominion over her son, which was so complete that the boy, who had by now reached the stage of adolescence, had become generally known as Missy. João Gaspar tried to draw him closer and win his confidence enough for them to have man-to-man talks about women. He tried taking him for walks that would end in Recife's street of women, the Rua do Fogo.

He was only partly successful. He did manage to elicit from his nephew—less from his own lips than from his adolescent diary—a few intimate facts concerning his first sexual adventures, which are told here as though they had been invented in the literary imagination of a semi-novelist, but which have some basis in the nephew's confessions recounted to me in turn by old Gaspar, Dona Sinhá's brother, in his drawling Wanderley voice. Gaspar trusted the discretion of another Wanderley; it would all stay in the family. Besides, José Maria's dignity would not be compromised by a possible revelation of the childhood experiences of a boy whose nature was fundamentally good.

It was also through Dona Sinhá's brother that I learned of the great friendship that linked José Maria while still a schoolboy with Paulo Tavares, who was already a young man. It was a schoolboy friendship, one of the most romantic that has ever drawn together, anywhere in the world, an unprotected boy and an adolescent youth who thought that he could and should be the protector from the fury of his schoolmates of a creature as angelic and delicate as José Maria was in those days. Some of them were real devils, cruel as only "normal" children can be to any child whose actions and appearance differ from their own. Children who are so conscious of what they suppose is their normality and who feel so superior to those of tastes and manners at variance with theirs are only anticipating the attitude of mediocre men who are suspicious of exceptional men and in league against them, attacking with the superiority of numbers and flinging insulting names and epithets at them. To those boys Dona Sinhá's son became Missy as soon as he entered school. The insinuation was that he was an avowed sissy, not a boy turning into a man through a process that was slightly different from the usual one.

Again I must stop and ask myself what kind of book I am writing, after all: an essay or a romance? A dissertation or a novel? The answer is that it is simply the story of a boy who, if he had never existed outside my own mind, existed in the ancestors of some of us and still exists within ourselves, in his relationships with his mother, his uncle, the black mammy who raised him during the last days of slavery, and the Mother of Waters who enthralled his Brazilian child's imagination; and in his education for the priesthood as the result of a religious vow, even though his vocation may have been imperfect.

In this chapter we shall recall José Maria's friendship, as an unprotected schoolboy among boys who were hostile to his almost girlish ways, with the big boy who took him under his wing and fought for him against the others, standing up to some of the most aggressive of them —bullies who took advantage of José Maria's frailness by shouting at Dona Sinhá's son that he was no man and no male; that he was a Missy and a sissy.

A perilous friendship it was, tinged from the start with an elusive hint of sex. There was something about it that smacked of forbidden love—very strictly forbidden indeed, in the time to which this awkwardly told story refers, although it must have been of some consolation to the youthful protector, already advanced in his reading, to know that there had been another time, an illustrious time in the history of man, when it had been the normal thing for the José Marias to be protected by the Paulo Tavareses. What had been abnormal in those days had been for a particularly sensitive or delicate boy to develop from adolescence into manhood without the protection of an older boy; and it had been the protector who, being his protégé's best friend and loving him a little as well as giving him his friendship and protection, initiated the youth into adult life.

Paulo Tavares, from what I was able to gather from conversations with old Gaspar, became so extremely protective toward the boy whom the others called Missy that he felt his friendly relationship with his almost angelic protégé slip a little, against his will, into something like that of the stronger sex toward the weaker. Not that Paulo was one of those degenerates who, wherever they may be found—in schools, aboard battleships, in seminaries, or among the troops—try to insinuate themselves into the exaggerated affection of those good-looking boys whose uncertain, hesitant movements, and even forms and faces, have something girlish about them. Becoming the protectors of the most attractive of these adolescents, they really aim to extract moments of epicurean pleasure of an almost purely physical nature from these transitory affections. The stronger boy plays the part of the stronger sex, the weaker that of the fair sex, in sentimental adventures which are only superficially of the kind censured by adults in almost all clearly patriarchal societies, whether primitive or modern.

João Gaspar was well acquainted with his nephew's protector. According to Gaspar, José Maria had been so spoiled and pampered by his mother that he had become in many ways as soft as a girl. However (he did not say so, but I guessed that it was probably true), if José Maria had not had Paulo's protection in school, he might well have slipped into the same degradation into which others have fallen before him.

The uncle, although neither Mason nor anticlerical,

was inclined to deprecate the strength of the religious ardor of certain adolescents who had made up their minds to become priests, particularly when the decision was less their own than that of a mother, father, or grandmother who had made up their minds for them— sometimes more from a desire to prevent other people from taking mother's, father's, or grandmother's place in the boy's affection than out of any purely mystical fervor. Sometimes, too, the adolescent's enthusiasm owes less to his absolute faith in Church doctrine than to absolute fidelity to a family vow that obliges him to be more and at the same time less than an ordinary individual. Such has been the story, throughout the four centuries of Brazil's history, of many a young Brazilian who has been made into a priest by his mother or his grandmother. A psycho-analyst would only scorn the aspect of the problem suggested here; but then, not everything in psychology can be clarified by psychoanalysis. If there are reasons that human reason does not comprehend, as a Frenchman once said, there are also aspects in the psychology of adolescents who grow up in Catholic, patriarchal environments like that of Brazil which none of the schools of psychoanalysis—neither that of Freud nor those of the sub-Freuds—seems to take into account.

Here I am wool-gathering again, spinning fancies about my story instead of simply telling it. The reader of a book like this one is not interested in such fancies, but only in what happened to the characters with whom he is already acquainted, in a novel in which love and friend-

ship, and even sex and religion, are inseparably mingled
from beginning to end. Various kinds of love are entan-
gled with as many different kinds of friendship, each in-
fluencing the other; and none of them is purely, unmistak-
ably this or that. Many men are sexual as well as racial
half-breeds, not only in their ideas, but in their sentiments as well; and not uncommonly such men achieve
greater fulfillment than do the supposedly pure of race,
of sex, of class, of ideas, and of sentiments. I said as
much one day at Dudu's to old Gaspar, who may have
pronounced his *l*'s like *r*'s and read nothing but old ro-
mances by Dumas, but who was nevertheless a most per-
spicacious old fellow. Gaspar agreed, sipping the fiery
brandy with which he whetted his appetite for Dudu's
delicacies, and said in his slow drawl: "That's the truth.
Take one of our own relatives, Cotegipe the Baron—being not pure-blooded, white Wanderley, but a mulatto,
was he or wasn't he more of a politician than all the pure
Wanderleys put together? Or look at another relation of
ours, Dona Francisca from Rio Formoso. She was too
mannish for a woman, but didn't she amount to more
than any of those prissy little plantation ladies? And José
Mariano, who was part gentleman and part rascal! Was
he or was he not more of a democrat and more of a politician than any politician in those days who was all gentleman or all rascal?"

To return to the case that concerns us here: to what
point did the relationship between protector and protégé,
between Paulo and José Maria, progress, in the days

when the friendship between the two was mingled with sexual attraction? It is not easy to tell now. Paulo would not have been likely to confess to Gaspar, much less to Dona Sinhá, that one day he had lost his head and kissed his frail protégé passionately on the mouth. The fact was merely noted, rather cabalistically, in José Maria's diary, which his uncle had kept. On that occasion—or so I should imagine, drawing certain deductions as a detective, on a purely psychological basis—Missy must almost have fainted. Who could tell, at this distance in time, what had caused the victim's quasi-swoon: astonishment at being sensually kissed, or the voluptuous abandonment of the "missy" in José Maria to the male aggression of his protector? It was no doubt true that the kiss (and perhaps the hug) had been followed by other kisses and other hugs; although from what I know of both Paulo and José Maria, the hugs had probably never gone to the extreme of sexual fulfillment but had only anticipated uncompleted acts—"necking," in modern American, which, if these suppositions are correct, forged the relationship between the two into an intense, even lyrical friendship pervaded, but not dominated, by their mutual sexual attraction. Such a relationship would of course be difficult —though not impossible, claim the sexologists—to maintain undefiled.

From Gaspar, who had been Paulo's confidant up to a point and who was the uncle of a José Maria who had always struck him as dangerously more like a girl than a boy, owing to the way Dona Sinhá had brought him up, I learned that his nephew had entered the seminary at the same time that Paulo had sailed for Europe. The coincidence was a significant one. Paulo had always wanted to be a doctor, but his decision to study medicine in Belgium or France had come as a surprise to his family, who would have preferred for him to pursue his studies in Bahia or in Rio. It seems that he first went to Belgium—I don't know why, exactly—and later settled in France. But I do not know for certain, nor could Gaspar enlighten me on that point. All that he knew was that Paulo had gone abroad almost without warning, leaving his father, and especially his mother, very lonely; and leaving Dona Sinhá's son José Maria, as we can well imagine, lonelier still.

I do not mean to imply that José Maria no longer had the love of Dona Sinhá, who herself missed Paulo. It almost seemed to her as though a piece of José Maria had been torn from him—and from herself, Sinhá, to whom her son was almost a second Christ Child.

It was not so much Paulo whom she missed as it was her son's schoolmate and protector, who had been in her eyes the substitute, in a certain area of the affections closed to the relationship of a boy with his mother, for the older brother that José Maria so sorely needed, having lost both father and grandfather. It is possible, however, that Sinhá, being so extremely attached to her only son, had begun to sense in Paulo an unwanted rival in that affectionate relationship of protector and protégé. She may actually have felt relieved at the departure of her rival for a distant land, whence his letters and post cards began to arrive romantically and innocuously. Mothers are so contradictory at times in their attitudes toward their children and the latters' relationships with other people that it is not to be wondered at that Dona Sinhá should have missed Paulo and at the same time felt relief at his absence.

Once Paulo was out of sight, José Maria's religious fervor took the form of such a poignant devotion to the Virgin Mary that this mystical filial love became greater than Missy's earthly love for Sinhá. Dona Sinhá noticed this; she was very observant. Let no one dare to suppose, however, that Dona Sinhá was touched even remotely by jealousy of the intense love that her son, now in the seminary, felt for the Virgin Mary. Her son's devotion to Mary was one in which his mother participated so whole-heartedly that the two loves seemed to Dona Sinhá to be fused into one. It was the future priest who must have struggled for some time with a stubborn sorrow, as he tried to forget his faraway friend by concentrating his thoughts with mystical tenderness on the saint to whose devotion his mother had pledged him from childhood. Perhaps in Olinda, watching the sea shade from green into blue as its waters grew deeper and farther away, his meditations wandered more than once to a mysterious country beyond the sea. He may have sinned against God and the Virgin Mary and longed to be kissed again by a man instead of only kissing, with dry, virgin lips—liturgically, seraphically—the feet of the saints. Perhaps. No one knows. Nor, in my conversations with Gaspar, did I ever venture so far in my speculations about his nephew.

It is true that the authentic backwoodsman who existed in Gaspar astonished me sometimes with his shrewd observations. It was as though Gaspar, who was foxy enough in his own way, had read his Dumas with more sagacious eyes than had most backwoodsmen of his day. Decidedly, not all of the Wanderleys are—like most of the Correias de Oliveiras of Pernambuco and the Machados of Alagoas—people whose intelligence has been gradually eroded by the insidious effect of life in decaying mansions on decaying plantations. Gaspar was capable of expounding subtleties that would have amazed the sophisticates of Rio or Recife. It was through those subtleties that I was able to advance farthest in my attempts to reconstruct certain aspects of the relationship between Dona Sinhá and the son who was destined for the priesthood, and the one between a defenseless José Maria and a Paulo who seemed to have evolved from the merely physical protector of a rather girlish boy into that boy's sentimental protector as well, adding to the friendship a little—but only a very little—forbidden love. For José Maria's devotion to the Virgin was impervious to all other passions.

Even at the risk of obscuring the narrative of this seminovel by adding to it part of an essay on methodology, I feel obliged to repeat once more that after I had begun by creating some purely imaginary characters for a novel, at least one of them had appeared before me, claiming to be real and demanding that I respect her as a person of flesh and blood. In this she was mistaken, but not entirely so. She did exist outside of my mind, but also, and more importantly, within it.

As a result, I had from a certain point on begun to write her story and that of her son in accordance with the precepts followed by the naturalistic school of writers. I had, however, added some touches which stem, with all their faults, as much from a poet's imagination as from that of a scientist or even from that of a detective, as has become commonplace recently among authors of so-called works of fiction who wish to give a more scientific, and specifically more psychological, character even to the biographies of saints.

What is the thesis of one such author? That a detective is better armed than a natural scientist to discover and verify any truth about human beings, because he has more freedom and is better prepared for the unknown, whatever it may be. Furthermore, the naturalist is less concerned with revealing the truth than with verifying laws, whereas the detective knows that exceptions also exist and that every human being is unique. Nothing, in fact, is more useful to this new kind of biographer than to follow the manuals on the art of detection, which teach us that no detail is insignificant, for the most trivial object or gesture or *lapsus linguae* may be the key to a discovery—the clue leading to a revelation.

7

HOW HAD I made the acquaintance of Dona Sinhá's brother, old Gaspar? It is time for me to explain that point.

Arriving at Dona Sinhá's house one rainy afternoon in May, I was met at the door by Amaro with the news that the old lady had gone out. She was helping another lady from São José do Ribamar decorate the image of the Virgin Mary for the feast day on the 30th. Dona Sinhá was known as an expert in that difficult art, assiduously cultivated by the residents of São José, the decoration of the images of saints for liturgical festivities. Her slender white fingers could coax wonders out of humble wild flowers. When she was given lilies, carnations, and roses from the Madalena and Ponte d'Uchoa gardens, the results were more wonderful still. There were those who valued her altar decorations more highly than the famous arrangements of Brother Ângelo, a little friar with the hands of a woman, who knew how to decorate crêches more beautifully than anyone else.

Amaro went into the house, and from the back of the drawing room an old man's voice, with a twang in it that could only belong to a Wanderley, invited me to come in and talk to him while I waited for Dona Sinhá. When I had joined him and sat down, Wanderley introduced himself as Dona Sinhá's brother from Olindeta Plantation, of

whom the old lady had already spoken to me. She had
told him that I was a relative and that my grandparents
had also come from Serinhaém. Did João Gasper remember Cousin *Maria Raymunda*? Well, this relative was *Ma-*
ria Raymunda's grandson from Mangueira Plantation
and the great-grandson of Manuel, known as "Tooth-
picks" because he used to spend hours at a stretch lying
in his hammock on the porch, sharpening toothpicks
with a penknife. It was interesting to hear this other Serinhaém Wanderley talk. He had the same nasal drawl as
the others; his voice was *exactly like the voice of my*
great-uncle Manuel da Rocha Wanderley, the son of
"Toothpicks" Wanderley.

It was commonly said around Serinhaém, not without
good reason, that the Wanderleys—owners of modest
plantations, for the most part, except for an occasional
grandly prosperous one like Rosário—were too lazy to do
anything, even to talk. The stouter ones, indeed, were too
lazy to walk. *It was known for a fact that fat Sô of Man-*
gueira Plantation used to keep his hunting boots on even
when he walked around half-dressed inside his house, or
lay sluggishly in his hammock making toothpicks with a
penknife, as his father had done before him. No one ever
saw him wearing slippers. He wanted to be ready to
mount his horse in case he felt the simple urge to def-
ecate. He would rise from the hammock and go down to
the orange grove next to the house, booted and on horse-
back, or to the nearby banana trees. He followed the no-
ble custom of defecating with his boots on, or else, like

63

the plantation ladies, in a urinal in his bedroom—one of those great, tall, lordly urinals, called "captains" because of their size, which were a well-known fixture in great-houses belonging to blue-blooded Wanderleys like the owners of Rosário and their relatives, the Wanderleys of Morim.

The master of Olindeta went on to tell me, rather ungallantly, that he was younger than his sister by about a year. I observed the trembling of his hands—aristocratic hands, like Dona Sinhá's. The tremor of the slender hands seemed to accentuate the tremor of the slow, nasal voice that sounded familiar to me because it was like the voices of other Wanderleys I knew, *relatives of my parents in Mangueira.*

It did not surprise me that his name should be Gaspar, João Gaspar. *The name Gaspar has been kept alive for centuries among the Brazilian Wanderleys in memory of the Dutch founder of the clan. For that matter, I have a sister named Gasparina. Along with the name, certain Nordic characteristics have been preserved in the more inbred Wanderleys, having resisted to this day, with amazing tenacity, the effects of the tropics and the long span of time dividing them from Europe. (Once a journalist from Rio, visiting our house for the first time, mistook the elder Freyre, my father, for an Englishman.)*

Since I still smoked cigarettes at that time, I offered blond old Gaspar an imported brand, which he brusquely refused. No; he smoked nothing but cigarettes filled with home-grown tobacco and rolled with his own hands. In that as in everything else, he, Gaspar de Rocha Wanderley, was the truest native son I had ever met; I was to make no mistake about that. Foreign ways weren't his ways. Whereupon he began to roll his Alagoas cigarette, ever so slowly, between his tremulous yet slightly voluptuous fingers. The tobacco was acrid, and so strong that it altered the scent of flowers mingled with incense that permeated Dona Sinhá's sitting room and reached as far as the front door—perfume from the fresh flowers invariably placed near the photograph of her dead son, whom she venerated as a saint, or something very like one; perfume from the incense which she saw that Amaro never neglected to burn in honor of the holy protectors of the house, and which, wafted from the chapel to the sitting room, was always mingled with the smell of roses.

As the churchbell of São José do Ribamar pealed out the hour of six, Amaro crossed himself and mumbled some prayers of which I, for one, could not understand a word. They may have been prayers in Latin, taught to him by the Penha friars. At that old Gaspar, half jokingly and half in earnest, called the boy a pickaninny altar boy. I perceived from this remark that Gaspar did not accompany his sister in her devotions, a fact which became still more apparent when he added: "That pickaninny of Sinhá's would be a bishop if he were white. He knows how to pray better'n a woman."

"It is only women who pray, Seu [1] Gaspar?"

"Men only pray when they're dying. I don't hold with

---

[1] *Seu*, a colloquial variant of *Senhor*, is a mildly respectful form of address which precedes a man's Christian name. The feminine equivalent is *Dona*.

men praying before their time has come, unless they
want to be priests and have done with it. But real priests
aren't men anyway. They're more like women. You might
say they go straight from being boys to being women
without ever being men, hardly. A cassock might just as
well be a skirt. Maybe the habit doesn't make the monk,
but it does make a woman out of any man who goes
around in a cassock before he's grown, and out of any
man who's a real priest." Gaspar emphasized the "real
priest," as though he considered false those priests who
could not resign themselves to sacrificing their manhood
on the altar of the Virgin.

Pointing to his dead nephew's photograph, he added:
"Just look at that little priest. He never knew what it was
like to be a man. After he stopped being a boy he turned
into a woman, or might just as well have. That was what
the young folks called him right here in Ribamar: Missy.
His mother brought him up that way, tied to her apron
strings. I tried every way I knew how to make a man out
of him, an honest-to-goodness man who would want to
ride and hunt foxes with the niggers and go swimming in
the Una River and deflower nigger gals and get 'em pregnant—a man who wouldn't want to be a priest. It wasn't
any use. I'd take that silly Zemaria to Olindeta, and he'd
no more ride a horse or play around with the nigger
women in the house than he'd fly to the moon. All he
wanted to do was sit in a corner reading old almanacs; and
then in the evenings he'd lead prayer meetings for the old
women in the chapel. Sometimes I'd catch him on the ve-

randa looking out over the cleared land as if he were
seeing things nobody else could see. He was a funny kind
of a boy. And it was the same way here. I tried over and
over to get him to come with me to the women's houses
on the Rua do Fogo—I'm a regular old bachelor, and I
know 'em all—but it wasn't a bit of use."

He puffed on his cornsilk cigarette. "People say Nhô
Quim from Maçangana [2] was the same way, only they

[2] Joaquim Nabuco ("Nhô Quim") was a distinguished diplomat, writer, and member of Parliament, an outstanding figure
in nineteenth-century Brazil. Although he had been born into
the wealthy slave-owning class of Recife (on Maçangana
Plantation, in 1849), Nabuco was an ardent abolitionist from
his earliest youth. While still in law school, he defended a
slave who had killed his master after being publicly whipped.
The prestige of his father, a senator, won him an entrée into
the diplomatic service; and he was posted as attaché in Washington and London before being elected a federal deputy under the aegis of the Liberal Party in 1878. Nabuco's defense of
emancipation, direct elections, and the admittance of non-
Catholics to Parliament jeopardized his political career and
induced him to go into exile in London. The British Anti-Slav-
ery Society sent him to Milan in 1883 as its representative to
the Congress for the Reform of People's Rights. Returning to
Brazil the following year, he resumed his career in politics
and was re-elected to Parliament, where he continued to
champion the abolitionist cause until the passage of the law
abolishing slavery (the "Lei Áurea") in 1888.

Nabuco was a loyal monarchist, although he favored the
liberalization and popularization of Brazil's monarchical sys-
tem. When the country became a republic in 1889 and Emperor Dom Pedro II was exiled to Europe, Nabuco retired
from political life. Shortly afterward, however, he agreed, at
the request of President Campos Salles, to serve as Brazil's

never made a priest out of him, good or bad. No one in
Maçangana ever got him to mount a horse or a woman,
or any other kind of animal. Nhô Quim was as slippery as
an eel. He always stuck close to his godmother, and it's
my opinion she was like Sinhá and wanted to make a
priest out of him. But she passed away, and Nhô Quim
went to Rio to be with his father, who was living at the
Court. The way I heard it, the French Court ladies took
the bashfulness out of him. One thing he never did learn,
though, was to ride a horse. And he never had a taste for
black women, like the rest of us country boys—and let
me tell you, there're no other women like 'em. I knew a
nigger woman here in São José—she was so good-looking she'd knock your eye out—who was crazy about Nhô
Quim. He was such a fine-looking fellow that gal lost her
head over him. And he didn't pay her no mind at all.
What a fine litter of mulattoes Nhô Quim could have had
out of that bitch! But no, all he did was talk a lot of
foolishness about how good the niggers were, and praise
the black mammies to the skies, and say the slaves ought
to be emancipated, and cuss the plantation owners who

---

advocate in a treaty dispute over the boundary of British Gui-
ana. (The disputed territory was divided into two equal parts
in 1904 by the arbiter, King Victor Emmanuel III of Italy.)

Nabuco was appointed ambassador to the United States in
1905. He and Secretary of State Elihu Root acted as joint
chairmen of the historic Third Pan-American Conference,
held in Rio de Janeiro in 1906. Returning to Washington,
Nabuco remained as ambassador until his sudden death in
1910.

had niggers whipped. And then he didn't have the nerve to get nigger women pregnant, even the ones who were so crazy about him they were ready to rip the clothes off him if he'd only lie down with 'em. Nhô Quim had a perfect build. Once I heard *Frederico, old João Ramos's son, tell about the time when his father went swimming in the Beberibe with Nhô Quim when Nhô Quim was a young fellow. He and João Ramos and I think Maciel Pinheiro and some other big-shot abolitionists all compared penises, and Ramos's and Nhô Quim's—"Belo Quincas's— were smaller than some of the others. They were just average, nothing special.* But all that kind of talk about the size of a man's member is just plain foolishness. I've gone swimming with a lot of fellows who had pretty sizable cocks. But when it comes right down to performance, I've seen some of those big ones fizzle out, while your friend, here, who doesn't have anything special to boast about in that department, took plenty of mulatto girls away from barons. From viscounts too. Yes, sir, from barons and viscounts. Not to mention a certain rich Portuguese comendador [3] here in Recife. I won't tell you who he was, because the family still lives in a mansion in Madalena. He used to cover his favorite mulatto girl with jewels as though she were a saint on an altar. And that mulatto devil fell for me so hard, even though I was just a country boy and didn't have any jewels or English pounds to give her, that I got to feeling sorry for the

---

[3] Honorific distinction corresponding to a high military rank or knighthood.

comendador. That girl wouldn't let me out of sight long enough to scratch the Portugee behind the ears the way he liked."

As I listened to him attentively, drinking in his drawling words and savoring his indiscretions, spoken in a nasal and slightly tremulous voice, Gaspar da Rocha Wanderley went on, beginning to be rather flattered by the interest he aroused in me with his recollections of himself as a boy on the Pernambuco Plantation in the old days, and of his exploits with colored women.

"That was the way I wanted to bring José Maria up: to be a man. To be like his uncle who, thank the Lord, was a real man. I may look like an old man to you, but I'm not a bit sorry to have been the woman-chaser I was. A woman-chaser, and, if you'll excuse the expression, a stud horse. Is that a sin? Sinhá was mortified at the way I turned out. She's such a saint and I'm such a sinner. But do you really think I sinned in the eyes of the Lord when I filled up the country around Olindeta with healthy mulattoes and straight-haired, yellow-headed niggers? I don't reckon I did. I'll tell you who *was* a sinner, because he didn't do his part by giving Brazil good strong mulatto men and sassy mulatto women—good-looking folks— and that was Nhô Quim Nabuco. But your caboclo [4] friend here did the work of two. I did my own part and Nabuco's too."

[4] Brazilian of mixed Indian and white blood; backwoodsman. The term is sometimes used symbolically to describe anyone who is "every inch a Brazilian," proud of his native roots.

After delivering himself of this speech, old Gaspar, his gestures as slow as his drawling, nasal Wanderley voice, began to roll his second cigarette. He called my attention to another photograph in the room.

"Do you know who that foreign-looking fellow is? A Brazilian born right here in Recife, but he's turned into a European. He was Zemaria's protector in school when they were boys. Zemaria always needed a protector: the other boys tormented the life out of him. The nickname they gave him here in the courtyard stuck to him all through school: Missy! That fellow in the picture was a monitor, and he was the one who kept the other boys from bothering Zemaria, just as if he had been his older brother. Zemaria was so crazy about him he didn't know what to do. If he'd been a girl he would have married him. He acted like a girl when he was with that fellow; and so did Sinhá. Zemaria was more than just a little St. Anthony [5] to her; he was practically a second Christ Child. But she thought of Tavares—that was the fellow's name—as a sort of romantic knight-errant. Tavares went to Belgium to study, Belgium or France, I don't rightly know which. Zemaria missed him so much he almost died. Without Tavares's company he was lonelier and more like a priest than ever. He stuck closer than ever to Sinhá and the saints. He was so unhappy it was enough to break your heart. Those two never saw each other again. Tavares wrote a lot of letters to Zemaria, and a lot

[5] *Santo-antoninho:* pet; darling.

of cards to Sinhá. He even sent me a post card with a view of Paris on it. But he only came back a long time after he had gone away to Europe, and he got here too late to find Zemaria alive. He put his arms around Sinhá and cried. Both of them were in mourning; he put on a brother's mourning for Zemaria. I had some long conversations with Tavares before he went back to Europe, and it didn't take me long to smell a Frenchwoman in his life. He told me all about it. And then he told me that if Sinhá wanted him to, he'd leave Europe, Belgium, the Frenchwoman, and everything else and come back here to live—and marry Sinhá! Sinhá didn't want to. I'll tell you more about Tavares some other day. That'll give us enough talk for a whole afternoon."

8

BEFORE LEAVING Dona Sinhá's house, I arranged to have lunch with old Gaspar some Thursday in the Pátio do Mercado—and where else but in the restaurant that belonged at that time to Dudu, who is no longer living. Gaspar knew the restaurant; he knew Dudu; he had known the restaurant before it had belonged to Dudu. He liked the sarapatel cooked by Dudu, who had a weakness for people from the interior of the state. The large, stout Dudu liked to hear stories about things that had happened on the old plantations, told by men who came in from the backcountry to see Recife movies, Recife women, Recife novelties, without ever staying in Recife for long. That was the life that he, Dudu, would have lived if he could: he would have come to Recife every so often, but he would have made his home in the country. A little sugar mill would have been enough to satisfy him. This business of living in Recife all the time didn't suit him at all. He hankered after the smell of the country; it made him sick to smell sea and salt water all the time. He longed to smell cane fields, and stables, and cattle.

That was the very life old Gaspar led. He came to Recife once in a while, holed up in some cheap little hotel so as not to scandalize his prim and proper sister with his homecomings at dawn after copious rounds of beer with the women in the boardinghouses. He spent most of his time, however, in the great-house in Olindeta. He attended country dances in Rio Formoso, feast-day celebrations and pilgrimages to the shrine of St. Amaro in Serinhaém, and religious processions in Ipojuca: a typical backwoodsman's life, according to Gaspar.

After telling me a little about himself, Gaspar da Rocha Wanderley, still dragging out his words as though it cost him more trouble than it did most people to pronounce them, began to speak about Paulo Tavares.

"He's a peculiar sort of a fellow, that Dr. Tavares. I don't think he even speaks our language any more, he's been away from Brazil for so long, living in Europe and talking that foreign gibberish all the time. He told me the whole story of his life the last time he was here. Nobody could have been more willing than he was to stay here for good, give up that French gal and all his foreign ways. But only if Sinhá agreed to marry him. And Sinhá said right away that it was impossible: 'I'm so much older than Tavares, I feel as if I were his mother. It's as though he were a brother of my little priest. How could I marry him?'

" 'Foolishness,' Tavares would say. 'It's only in an old-fashioned place like Brazil that you still run into this custom of having young girls marry old men. In Europe that's only for actors, artists, people like that. Or when old lords marry young governesses. No one in Europe thinks anything about it when a young man marries a lady of a certain age. It's natural. It's the thing to do.' "

Gaspar went on with Tavares's story as though he were telling a romantic narrative: "There wasn't any way in the world to persuade Sinhá to agree to marry Zemaria's friend. She said Tavares was almost as holy to her as the little priest; that without Tavares, Zemaria might have died a lot sooner than he did, and not ever had the luck to be a priest. That was why she didn't dare even to think of marrying him. She wanted to remember him as Zemaria's friend forever—someone who existed outside her common, everyday world. In Angelim, when Zemaria was already so sick, he'd cough and say: 'Mamma, the person I'd most like to see, besides you, is Paulo.' He meant Tavares."

Dona Sinhá had written to Tavares begging him to come and visit the little priest, who was dying so slowly and always asking for him. Old Gaspar reconstructed in his own way, substituting *r*'s for *l*'s, the conversations between his nephew, who was dying of consumption, and his mother, the afflicted Dona Sinhá, who never left his side—conversations which reflected the young priest's preoccupation with his distant friend:

" 'Oh, Mamma, it would be so nice if Paulo could come. But I know it's hard for him. He's not rich, and a ticket on the Royal Mail is expensive. But I might feel better, if he came. Not really well, Mamma. You wouldn't even want me to get well. The end is coming, and Our Lady wants me near her. She is my mother too, Mamma. You'll have to share me with her and be patient—I'll wait for you near Our Lady and Jesus. I've accomplished my mission on earth and done what you wanted, Mamma. You wanted to see the day when I'd be a priest saying mass, hearing confessions, baptizing, marrying, giving extreme unction. You didn't see all that, but you did see me all ready to become a priest. Now it's Our Lady's turn to have me near her. I'll wait for you there. We can't go together. God wants each of His creatures to die apart from the others. Each one of us has to die all alone.' "

Tavares didn't come. Zemaria, ravaged by fever, died in Dona Sinhá's arms, with her name and that of the other Dona Sinhá—the one he knew was waiting for him in Heaven"—on his dry, tubercular lips.

Tavares did not arrive until some months later. He went immediately to São José do Ribamar and put his arms around Dona Sinhá in tears. They went to the cemetery together to visit the little priest's grave. Tavares took so many flowers with him that the coachman was amazed. Never had any coach in Recife carried so many flowers for the dead or the living.

The man who had become a foreigner spent many days in his former home revisiting his fondest old haunts, but he devoted most of his time to consoling his widowed mother and the other mother, Dona Sinhá, for Zemaria's death. He told João Gaspar, whom he had made his confidant, that Zemaria's image was always before his eyes: it was as though it accompanied him everywhere he went. He had never felt so deep an attachment for anyone as for the vanished friend of his adolescent days, who seemed to rise from the dead for him alone but shrank from the touch of his hands, which eagerly sought more than an image in the image he had evoked. Dona Sinhá's company seemed to soothe his poignant yearning for José Maria. In her he found traces of his departed friend: the sorrowful smile, the eyes like those of a girl, the hands that he remembered as being light as feathers.

Yes, Tavares would have liked to remain in Brazil, cut all his ties with Europe, and be a Brazilian again instead of a European—but only if his nostalgia for Zemaria could take the form of union with the little priest's mother. He talked about this so often to old Gaspar that the latter began to fear that the "foreigner" might be losing his mind. Not that he disliked Dr. Tavares; he was a fine man, a doctor who didn't put on airs. He willingly listened to João Gaspar talk for hours at a time, and he opened his heart in turn to the Olindeta Wanderley as if he had found in Dona Sinhá's brother an ideal friend who could understand, as well as anyone ever could understand, how much he missed José Maria and longed to marry the mother of the little priest. When recalling these conversations with Tavares, João Gaspar admitted to me that he never could rightly understand what was making the "foreign fellow" so unhappy. Nevertheless, the fact was that after listening to him for so long, he had learned more than anyone else about Paulo's life in Europe, and in Brazil too, before he had gone to study in Belgium or in France. In his conversations with João

Gaspar, Tavares recounted interesting episodes from his Brazilian past and his experience in Europe. I have attempted, in my turn, to reconstruct the historical as well as biographical context of these not uninteresting accounts by filling in some of the gaps in the old gentleman's narrative from my own imagination, assisted on the one hand by what little I know of psychology and on the other by my knowledge of Brazil's past. It has been a labor of love, love for a subject which I deemed worthy of being incorporated into a novel, even though it is a novel with very little plot—in short, a semi-novel.

9

DONA SINHÁ, at whose house in the Pátío of São José do Ribamar I was such a frequent visitor during long months of research, or rather detection, was convinced that José Maria had been born for the priesthood. He could never have been anything but a priest.

"But what about your promise to Our Lady that he would be a priest?" I ventured to ask one afternoon after she had permitted me to read, with her eyes fastened upon me, some of the papers her son had left, which she kept under lock and key. The old lady replied that she had made such a promise only because she had discovered her son's vocation when he was still only a child.

"José Maria," she explained, "never played rough games with the other boys. Running and racing, jumping up and down and getting all hot and tired, letting off firecrackers on St. John's Day, riding horses at Olindeta, wanting to go out in a boat with the fisherman for days at a time—nothing like that ever took him away from me. He did like to draw, and he liked to fly kites that he made himself from the window of the house. And he liked to sit and play with matchboxes and shoe boxes, or with a stalk of flowers, or an empty scent bottle, or picture of toys he cut out of the magazines. That was the kind of thing that kept him at home with me. When he did go out, it was just around here with Inácia. He loved to go to Father Zacarias's house and to Penha Church. The friars were very fond of him, and so was Father Zacarias."

Dona Sinhá went on to say that whenever her son went to Olindeta with his uncle, all he thought about was going back to São José do Ribamar. His world was there in Ribamar, not in the country. He didn't see anything interesting about the sugar mill grinding cane, or the squeaky ox carts, or Uncle Gaspar's fat horses. All that interested him was São José do Ribamar, where he could watch the ocean and wade in the water that came from far out at sea, from the blue, beyond the green.

José Maria was beside himself with happiness on the day that Dona Sinhá, after admonishing him to be ever so careful, let him go out in a jangada [1] for the first time with an old caboclo fisherman who had long years of experience in the coastal waters of Pernambuco, the blue as well as the green. The little boy begged the old fellow to take him out to the blue water that he had looked at from a distance for so long. He wanted to see what it looked like up close. Afterward he told Dona Sinhá that the blue water was even prettier up close than from far away, without explaining what he meant. He told his mother how tiny Recife had looked like a city in a crêche, with its church towers sticking up among the trees. He had seen the Church of São José do Ribamar shrink smaller and

[1] Fisherman's catamaran.

smaller until it was just the size of a toy. And they had gone up to a big steamer with a blue-and-crimson flag, which the old fisherman had told him was a British steamer with the English flag.

Dona Sinhá had waited for him with her rosary in her hands and her heart in her mouth, fearful of the perils of that adventure and regretting that she had ever consented to José Maria's being taken out so far in a fishing boat. But the Ribamar fisherman were there to calm her fears.

"Don't you worry, ma'am. There ain't nothin' as safe on the water as our Brazilian jangadas," said one of the oldest fishermen around those parts, encouragingly. His name was Pedro das Neves, and it was said that he had once caught a glimpse of the Mother of Waters and had resisted the lure of her songs by chanting an Ave Maria himself.

When José Maria came home after his first adventure at sea, Dona Sinhá covered him with kisses and petted and fussed over him as though he had been to Africa and back. She vowed to herself that José Maria would never repeat that exploit. The little boy was in seventh heaven. For days, weeks, months even, he talked about nothing but his boat trip. He was so full of it that Pedro das Neves had the audacity to hint that perhaps Dona Sinhá's son had been born to be a sailor, and not a priest after all. When this remark reached Dona Sinhá's ears, it provoked her to anger: let Pedro look after his own loud-mouthed children and have the grace to keep his opinions about

José Maria to himself. What José Maria wanted to be was a priest. He wanted to say mass, to hear confessions, to baptize babies, and, above all, to fish for souls for the Virgin Mary and for Jesus and not, like Pedro das Neves, for ciobas and ray to sell in the market.

José Maria's favorite adventure—putting out to sea in a jangada with experienced fishermen in water that was more blue than green—was repeated more than once. The boy always returned in such a state of bliss that Dona Sinhá occasionally yielded to his pleas to go out again. After all, jangadas really were safer than ordinary fishing boats. One never heard of a jangada's being shipwrecked, only of barges, big ships, even English liners. As for the peril of the Mother of Waters, Dona Sinhá, when it came to taking her son out beyond the reefs, entrusted him to the care of only such fishermen as belonged to the Brotherhood, who crossed themselves every time they put out to sea, and who could sing the Ave Maria and recite the Credo in case Iemanjá rose from the green waters to seduce Christians and lead good men astray. She had been told that Iemanjá appeared only in green water, never in blue. Without knowing this, José Maria sought only the blue water when he went out in a jangada. Dona Sinhá thought she saw in this preference a confirmation of her son's religious vocation. Blue was Our Lady's color. The roof of Our Lady of Penha Church was painted blue. Blue was the color of the most important promises to the saints: men promised to wear blue neckties; women and children promised to dress only in blue and white, or blue and black. Blue was also the color of the sashes worn by boys who were being educated for the priesthood. That was how José Maria had dressed ever since he was very small—ever since his mother had promised Our Lady that he would be a priest—when Dona Sinhá had made him walk in religious processions, filled with maternal pride at the sight of her pretty little son dressed just like a miniature priest, with a blue sash so wide that many an elegant woman could have used it to trim her best party dress more showily than if it had been hand-made lace from Ceará.

One day I asked João Gaspar whether José Maria had been a good pupil in school and in the seminary. João Gaspar said yes, he had been a very good one. He was by no means lacking in intelligence, and as for his memory, his schoolmasters were astonished at its power of retention. "The memory of an angel," people called it admiringly. It was wonderful how accurately José Maria could memorize his lessons.

Dona Sinhá's brother would not go so far as to claim that his nephew had been good at figures. He had had a hard time with arithmetic. But when it came to Portuguese, Latin, or Bible history, he absorbed knowledge with a facility that his schoolmasters marveled at in a boy who was so shy that some adults, seeing him for the first time, thought that he was retarded. He was not retarded at all. You could tell by looking him in the eye, even before he said a word, that behind all that childish stubbornness and timidity lurked a shrewdness that was just as susceptible to suggestions from the world as it was prone to daydream.

Not even the minutest quirks of nature escaped his curiosity. The Largo fishermen taught him so much about fish that he outshone all of the other Ribamar children in that particular branch of natural history. He collected shells as eagerly as other boys collect stamps, grouping them by size, form, and color. He loved to look at them, with a sensuous admiration in which the voluptuousness of a budding artist blended with the scientific awareness of a budding naturalist. Every so often José Maria would pour fresh sea water over his shells, caring for them almost as lovingly as he cared for his fish and his baby birds. It was a sign that the shy little boy, dedicated by his mother to the austere service of God, was inclined to adopt a scientific attitude toward things and animals. His aptitude was for the natural sciences, particularly for the study of anything having to do with the sea.

Dona Sinhá once told me that her son was even sensitive to the different sounds of the ocean, which changed with the phases of the moon—so sensitive that he could distinguish one from another from a long way off. It was as though he collected the sounds made by the waves as they met the shore after breaking on the reefs, as they broke on the beaches where Dona Sinhá let him gather shells and sea creatures on afternoons when the sun was mild, warning him to be careful of the Portuguese men-of-war, which could sting so terribly when it was the foot of a delicate house-bred child wandering innocently along the beach who was caught in their blue—ominously blue—filaments. José Maria knew very well that his aristocratic, pampered little feet were very different from the feet of the wild children who grew up on the streets of São José and the beaches of Ribamar, or the feet of the fishermen, who were bronzed all over their bodies by the sun on the high seas, or the feet of the half-breed jangadeiros, feet that would have no truck with sandals, such was their greed for total liberty, their thirst for salt sea water, their hunger for sandy beaches. Once he told his mother that some impudent boys, watching him run barefoot along the beach, had hooted at him and shouted: "He's got feet like a girl's! He's got feet like a girl's!" The barefoot urchins may have flung worse insults than that at the boy who had feet like a girl's. At any rate, José Maria was overjoyed one day, shortly after he had come back from a week at Olindeta during the height of the cashew season, when, after watching him scratch one toe of his left foot for some time without stopping, Inácia announced: "Massa Zemaria's got chiggers!" Sure enough, he did have chiggers.

All at once José Maria felt a little less different from the other children, less like a boy with girl's feet. He had chiggers! Sinhama dug out the insects with a bright new needle sterilized in a candle flame. The woman was as painstaking as she could be, making sure to extract the chiggers whole and putting whitewash in the tiny holes, which bled hardly at all, so skillfully did she perform that delicate operation. All the rest of that afternoon José Maria enjoyed a pleasant little itch in the toe which had been so expertly tended by the Negro servant.

10

JOÃO GASPAR da Rocha Wanderley had impressed me on one occasion as being fanatically anticlerical. I ventured to inquire whether he was a thirty-third-degree Mason. He replied emphatically that he was not; he belonged to a religious fraternity, in fact, although he never marched in its processions except to accompany the funeral of a member of the brotherhood or his widow.

Not that he didn't enjoy a good procession. He liked the Ipojuca processions, and he had never forgotten the ones he had seen when he was a boy and had gone to visit an uncle who was studying in Olinda. He remembered watching them file slowly down the Varadouro Hill, the priests singing chants that he had never heard again since then. Perhaps they had gone out of style, he added, with the faintly ironic smile that is so typical of those Wanderleys who are less stout, heavy, and mentally retarded than their relatives. Perhaps it was that self-same smile which Cotegipe took with him, from a Bahia that was formerly a part of Pernambuco, to the Court and his debates with Zacarias.[1]

[1] Zacarias de Gois e Vasconcelos, territorial governor, federal deputy, senator, and a member of the Council of Ministers during the Second Empire, eloquently defended the Church in the Bishops' Question (*quo vide*) in the Senate against the distinguished senator and imperial minister João Mauricio Wanderley, Baron Cotegipe. Both men were born in Bahia in

Why, I wondered, did Gaspar seem so anticlerical? Was it because the Church had wanted to make a priest out of the nephew whom Gaspar, without legitimate off-spring of his own, had counted on to succeed him in Olindeta? Gaspar had evidently hoped that José Maria would be a son to him, and that he would one day take from his uncle's shoulders the burden of Olindeta Plantation, which had belonged to the family for generations. He had hoped that José Maria would grow up to resemble him— that he would be even fonder of women than of horses; that he would love to watch sugar ripening in the cane-brakes and then being ground in the mill; love to hear the creaking ox carts, and modinhas [2] sung to the guitar by mestizo field hands who could strum a guitar as skillfully as they could shoot paca [3] with a rifle. In Gaspar's opinion, no chicken or duck or turkey or suckling pig could match the flavor of a paca caught by his men and roasted by his Negro women.

Instead of growing up to be a Wanderley of the right sort, his nephew turned out to be a virginal lad who was frightened of women and horses. Why did the São José street urchins call him Missy? Because ever since her husband had died, Sinhá had practically lived in church

---

1815; both were graduated from law school in Olinda; and both were members of the Conservative Party in their later years.

[2] Popular songs.

[3] A mammiferous rodent with brown spotted fur and tender, flavorful meat.

and had always dragged the boy in after her. She did nothing but go to mass and confession, take communion, tell her rosary beads, attend novenas, dress her boy up like a priest while he was still nothing but a child, and let his hair grow long like the hair of the angels on the altars and the little girls in St. Joseph's Academy. Had the boy ever had a vocation for the priesthood? He, Gaspar, had his doubts. "Deformation" was the word he used to describe the influence exerted over his nephew by Dona Sinhá and her allies, the foreign monks. Sinhá had deformed her son and turned him into the kind of boy who could never be anything but a priest. If he had been separated from his family, Gaspar thought, José Maria would eventually have become alienated from his own mother —and all because of his exclusive love for the Church and the saints. João Gaspar found it quite understandable that in big families, with eight, ten, or twelve children, one son should be brought up to be a priest or a monk, or one daughter to be a nun. The Church in Brazil needed white people of good stock for its ranks, and among ten or twelve children there was always one with at least some inclination—and at times a whole-hearted love—for the religious life. But that Sinhá should have promised to sacrifice her only son to the Church before she could possibly know for sure whether or not the boy had a vocation was an error for which Gaspar could not forgive his sister. He blamed it on the foreign monks, whom she had obeyed unquestioningly ever since her girlhood days as a student in St. Joseph's Academy, that very St. Joseph's which had been the residence of the beautiful and celebrated Sister Virgínia who, according to local gossip, had been visited there rather frequently by Friar Vital after he had been made a bishop. He, João Gaspar, did not for a moment believe that there had been anything resembling a love affair between the bishop-friar and the teacher-nun. Quite the contrary. Dom Vital had been "a real priest," simply incapable of indulging in any hanky-panky with nuns or anyone else. What was more, he had been fanatically devoted to Our Lady. It was for Our Lady's sake that he had wanted to be a saint. When he was made a bishop, his first act was to weed out the old priests, large numbers of whom had concubines or were affiliated with Masonic lodges, and replace them with young men who belonged only to the Church and had no attachments—not even to parents or brothers and sisters—except the ties that bound them to the Church, the Pope, the saints, and the bishops. Gaspar admired Dom Vital—"That man was a real priest!"—but he had no use for foreign monks.

Sinhá had studied at St. Joseph's Academy and had fallen under the influence of the little Frenchified Capuchin director and the French nuns at the school. Gaspar wondered why Sinhá had not become a nun herself; it might have been a good thing for everyone if she had. But she had not become a nun; instead, she had married a dim-witted fellow with a bachelor's degree, a pompous, naïve youth from Belém do Pará, who had learned very little about law in Pernambuco. The only thing he understood something about was herbs and Amazon jungle medicine, and he stubbornly refused to consult doctors or take drugstore medicine. He fell ill of some mysterious disease not long after they were married, and since a doctor was called in only after his sickness was far advanced, when Dona Sinhá learned of it, the poor paraense [4] died two days later, leaving José Maria an orphan when he was the size of a Baby Jesus—the same size and with almost as much prestige, in his widowed mother's house, as a Baby Jesus. José Maria became everything in life to Sinhá, who, dressed in black and wrapped in widow's veils for many months, never left her son and the elder Wanderley, her father (who died in his turn a year and a half later), except to go to church. When, after her father's death, Sinhá moved from the mansion on the Rua do Alecrim to a smaller house in the Square of São José do Ribamar, the St. Joseph's nuns counseled her to go to the Capuchins at Penha Church to confess, to ask for guidance from the head of the friars, and to avoid priests who were Masons. It was in this environment that José Maria began to crawl and babble his first words, to play patty-cake, to smile at his mother, and to be cared for and petted by the plantation Negroes whom Sinhá had brought with her from Olindeta. She had been accompanied to her new home by a maid and a little pickaninny, both of whom she kept on a tight rein. In this Dona Sinhá resembled her relative, *Dona Fran-*

[4] Native of the northern Brazilian state of Pará.

cisca of Rio Formoso. It was a wonder that she did not
give orders to the very saints whose images she had
grouped according to hierarchical rank in the huge jacarandá shrine that she had brought from the plantation.
Once they had been arranged in good order, Sinhá expected the saints to be useful to her child in every way
they could: to watch over him and preserve him from
Masons and voodoo women. St. Lucia was to protect his
eyes, St. Blaise his throat, and St. Benedict was to see that
he was not bitten by snakes or stung by scorpions. All of
them were to guard him zealously against the evil eye of
envious women. One of these, an ancient inhabitant of
the Pátio do Têrço, was reputed to have such a fearful
power of drying up pepper plants in the yards and making children sick than whenever she watched a woman
suckling her child, the milk curdled in the baby's mouth.

Notwithstanding all of this divine protection, José Maria fell ill one day, as we already know. He had begun to
speak his baby Portuguese when the sickness attacked
him; he had left the toddling stage behind and had begun
to explore the whole house on his own precarious little
feet. Now he wore rompers and used a little white porcelain potty trimmed in pink. He smiled whenever some
friendly adult teased him (if Dona Sinhá was not in the
room) by touching, or pretending to touch, his little penis.

Sickness blighted José Maria just when he had reached
the most endearing stage of babyhood. He became a sad
and listless little boy whom nothing had the power to
amuse. João Gaspar told me that it was at his insistence

that Dona Sinhá consulted a doctor. The doctor arrived, the medicine followed, and a long, hard battle against José Maria's sickness ensued. But at no time did Dona Sinhá put her entire trust in the physicians and their medicine—expensive medicine with lovely foreign names, the best available in Europe. She appealed to her old Olindeta saints and to the new Italian saints whom she worshipped in the Church of Our Lady of Penha, patron saint of Recife's tradespeople. She sought help from every saint she could think of, especially from Our Lady of Carmen, José Maria's protectress in memory of her husband from Pará, who had been a Carmelite lay brother. When José Maria's illness dragged on and the neighbors began to console Dona Sinhá—that was the way it was; children as good as José Maria never grew up: Jesus wanted them near him—the afflicted mother, devoted as she was to Our Lady, promised the Mother of God that she would give her José Maria to Mary for the service of God and the Church if the little boy would only get well.

The Penha and Carmo friars must have approved of her vow, judging by the frequency of their visits to Dona Sinhá's house and the considerable sums she gave to both monasteries. Evidently she dreamed of her son's becoming not merely a priest, but a Carmelite or Capuchin friar. A priest might become a friar, and her vow was expressed in general terms: once he was cured, José Maria would be set apart for the priesthood. João Gaspar never became reconciled to that vow.

The old master of Olindeta had, as we know, already departed this life. João Gaspar had taken over the fields of sugar cane, the mill, the Negro men and women, and the oxen and horses inherited from the elder Wanderley. But he never got the better of his widowed sister, nor could he wrest from her control the nephew whom he had dreamed of installing in the great-house at Olindeta to be a true plantation owner, like so many other Wanderleys from southern Pernambuco. Olinda was destined to win out over Olindeta. Let us not, however, anticipate our story.

11

JOSÉ MARIA recovered. From that day on, Dona Sinhá's absorbing occupation in life was to prepare her son to fulfill his mother's mystic, holy, religious vow. She took care to keep him away from other children, whom he was already inclined by temperament to avoid. She kept him away from girls and women, from parties, dances, and country festivals. She marked him with the seal of his destiny, dressing him from babyhood in blue and white and making him accompany the altar of the Virgin Mary in religious processions, garbed like a priest in miniature.

All of this was part of a detailed, systematic process: the formation of a boy for the priesthood before the time came for him to enter the seminary. I use the word "formation" in an attempt to be objective in dealing with such a difficult case. But "deformation" was the word used by João Gaspar, the uncle of the little priest who had not, according to Gaspar, chosen his own way of life but merely accepted, meekly and passively, the destiny his widowed mother, who was wholly dedicated to her son and determined to dominate him for his own good, had chosen for him.

His uncle could never resign himself to this state of things. For Gaspar—although he was, as we know, younger than Sinhá among the few children sired by the former master of Olindeta—had dreamed of bequeathing the house and the sugar mill to his nephew. Gaspar had tried to tear the boy away from what he thought of as the pernicious yoke of Sinhá and the monks; he had tried to lure José Maria away to his own masculine, rustic way of life and instill in him his own fondness for women and horses, cane fields and country dances.

Even though he was no naïve, simple-minded back-woodsman, Gaspar was at a distinct disadvantage in this unequal battle against the simple country girl whom the French nuns of St. Joseph's Academy and the Italian friars of Penha had turned into a woman of Recife who was rather sophisticated in her manner of being a woman and a Catholic. It was not only the nuns and friars who had influenced her; the whole subtle climate was raised to a higher level by the law students and professors who came from all parts of the country, adding luster to the capital of Pernambuco with their various kinds of learning, and was stimulated by the presence of actors and actresses, violinists, and pianists who had been given contracts in Europe for the long entertainment season at the Apolo and Santa Isabel theaters.

After meeting Dona Sinhá, an old lady still in complete possession of her faculties, it was not difficult for me to imagine the Dona Sinhá who, convinced that she was acting for the Virgin Mary herself, and aided by the French nuns of St. Joseph's and the Italian friars of Penha, had spun about her son, whose nature was essentially feminine rather than masculine, a whole subtle web of inducements which had led him to sacrifice his sex—which, perhaps from birth, was more sweetly feminine than harshly masculine—and to put himself at the exclusive, absolute, even heroic service of the Virgin and the Church. It is possible, of course, that in so doing Dona Sinhá was only contributing to a firm vocation, although vocations for the Catholic priesthood are often a mass of contradictions. The most masculine of men have been called by the Church and by Christ to His Service, at the cost of such a complete and voluntary sacrifice of their sex that it is as if they had been marked at birth for that service. No one could have been less like Dona Sinhá's son, in the way in which he had grown from a boy into a man and from a seminary student into a friar, than the Dom Vital whom she so much admired. His virginity —which had no doubt been sorely tried, for he had been the son, and not merely the grandson, of plantation owners in També—was never lacking in masculine vigor: a vigor that was sublimated in an almost militant devotion to the Virgin and the Church.

For this reason I was never entirely convinced by João Gaspar da Rocha Wanderley's arguments against his sister and the priests, who, he claimed, had made a priest out of his nephew by deforming his nature from childhood for that purpose. Even if José Maria's upbringing had been altogether different, I do not think that he would ever have been more than an inept substitute, at best, for his uncle in the management of the Olindeta mansion and mill, or that he would ever have had his uncle's enthusiasm for Negro and mulatto women or his expert eye for horseflesh.

Not that I entirely believe the saying that good men are born, not made; or that other one about "as the twig is bent, so is the tree inclined," but neither am I in agreement with the environmentalists, according to whom environment alone determines an individual's character, future, and virtues, or lack of them.

João Gaspar bolstered his arguments with examples, some of which were blood-curdling indeed, of parents who had twisted their children's natures out of their natural shape, all for the sake of vows that the parents had made to the saints and the Virgin, and at the cost of sacrifices which, he believed, must surely be repugnant to the saints and to the Virgin. Furthermore, he did not hesitate to include his own sister among their number. While listening to João Gaspar da Rocha Wanderley expound on the subject, I sometimes mentally broke down his Brazilianized family name into the original Dutch, observing in Gaspar, for all that he insisted on representing himself as a plain man of the Brazilian backwoods, a trace of his ancestor Gaspar van der Lei, who, as tradition has it, abandoned his Calvinist faith in seventeenth-century Brazil and became a Catholic in order to marry a plantation owner's daughter from a family which was even then an old one in New Lusitania. I could not help thinking that there was in João Gaspar something secretly rationalistic—something of the Calvinism, Protestantism, anti-Catholicism, which had been passed down since the beginning of the seventeenth century by successive Wanderley Gaspars, Maurícios, and João Maurícios who, while to all appearances thorough-going Catholics, were still more than a little Protestant, rationalistic, antipapist, antiliturgical, even antipoetic, at heart. Perhaps the founder of the family had never really stopped being a Protestant.

Never did I surprise in João Gaspar any sign of a penchant for poetry, any lyrical effusion to belie the rationalistic traits to which some of the Brazilian Wanderleys seem to have clung since the seventeenth century. When it came to colored women, however, João Gaspar was the very negation of the South African Boer; but only up to a point. He would not hear of any Wanderley's marrying a Negro woman or a dark mulatto. Living with one was another matter; and the natural outcome of such a union would be a "love child"—a bastard whom the father would protect but never recognize. In this, Gaspar's racism was not so different from that of the Boer, after all.

I set down these observations in order to record here one, at least, of the "terrible examples" which João Gaspar quoted as arguments against his sister, accusing her of virtually turning her son José Maria into a girl, so that the young man was left with little alternative, once he had reached adolescence, but to be a priest whether he had a vocation or not. There was nothing for it but for José Maria to become a priest, since he was no longer capable of having a normal masculine sex life. The Chinese, contended João Gaspar, deformed their women from babyhood by forcing their feet into hobbles, which kept them from growing normally. That was what Sinhá had done, not merely to her son's feet but to his hands and his sex as well: she had forced them into figurative hobbles, which had prevented them from growing into the feet, hands, and sex of a normal adult. Once he had been twisted out of shape, concluded the nasal voice of my Wanderley relative—who sometimes gave me the impression of having preserved within his Catholicism the Protestant astringency of his Dutch ancestors—poor José Maria was obliged to become a priest. What else could he expect to do in this life but say mass, marry couples, and baptize infants? And since that was so, was he or was he not a victim of his mother, and of the French nuns and Italian friars who had her under their thumb? I noticed that when João Gaspar said "Italian," referring to the Penha friars, and "French" when referring to the St. Joseph nuns, he emphasized the adjectives, as though giving vent to this aversion as a good caboclo—for caboclo he was in his own eyes, despite his red hair and Nordic blue eyes—for anything foreign.

It was with the same rancor toward foreigners that he said to me one day: "I'll tell you some stories that will prove to you that those foreign monks are up to no good. Brazil ought to drive out the whole funny-talking lot of 'em. Monks are no good. The Catholic Church doesn't need monks, and it doesn't make any difference whether they're foreign or homegrown. The Church doesn't need monasteries and convents, and it doesn't need nuns. Almost every nun living in a convent today was shut up there against her will by her parents or her brothers. As often as not they just wanted to get their hands on the poor thing's fortune."

Gaspar went on to tell me the story of one Sister Paula, whom his father had met in the streets around the Court in Rio de Janeiro. *Poor Paula used to wander through the streets of Catete and Glória. She had come from a good family of plantation people. Her father and brothers had plotted, by shutting her up in the Convent of the Ajuda, to get possession of most of the fortune she had inherited from her mother. How had they succeeded in consummating this outrageous deed, which was once an all too common occurrence? With the help of the prioress of the convent! The unfortunate girl was taken from the country to the Court—that is, to the convent—in a closed box with a few air holes punched in it to enable her to breathe. Paula tried in every way she could to keep from having to take the veil; but take the veil she did. She became a nun, but she ran away three times. Three times she escaped and went back home, and each time the family took her back to the convent as a prisoner. Every time the girl was caught by her father and brothers and taken back to the convent, the old nuns punished and tortured her, until she lost her mind. Her wicked brothers took away everything that had belonged to her, and she was abandoned without a fortune, without a family, without even a family name. When she was old and her health had been broken, the Ajuda Convent nuns let her*

out to beg for bread in the streets and do a little sewing to
sell. Besides the sewing, the poor madwoman, who had
once been a gently bred plantation lady, had learned how
to make flowers out of little feathers, and wax figurines,
and clothes for the Christ Child to wear on feast days.
When my father was a chief sergeant and lived in Rio, it
was Paula who always set up the manger at Christmas-
time and decorated the image of the Christ Child more
beautifully than anyone else could have done.

Gaspar's father had met the old lady at Court. It was
there that he saw her dressing up the Christ Child and
kissing the image of the Baby Jesus over and over. "I
think," the old man used to say, "that the image was not
only Jesus to that poor crazy woman, but the child she
had wanted to have and couldn't because her father and
brothers had plotted with the Ajuda nuns to shut her up
in the convent against her will. Poor girl!"

"A terrible story!" Gaspar said, repeating what his
father had told him. Gaspar told me the story—which
was a terrible one, certainly, and at least partly true—
with his nephew in mind, obsessed by the idea that he too
had been forced, so to speak, into a religious life. He
blamed José Maria's mother and the French nuns and
Italian friars who, according to João Gaspar, were always
after boys and girls from good Brazilian families whom
they could turn into priests, monks, and nuns whether
the young people had any vocation or not. João Gaspar
thought that it was not so much a question of their
money. The real reason was this: if the Church could

assume control of the best families in this way, by tying every one of them to a convent or a monastery through a nun whose long hair they cut off, making her bald for life, or a boy whom they tonsured in order to brand him, also for life, as a captive slave of the Pope, then it would virtually control Brazil. If the young people were no longer interested in being priests and nuns, and if their fathers and mothers were not so eager as they had been in the old days for every family to give a priest or a friar or a nun to the Church, then it was up to the Church, acting through the French nuns and the Italian friars, to make up for this lack of zeal by taking Brazilian boys and girls away from their families and impressing them into service, if necessary by force. João Gaspar did not think that this was right. It was these remarks that led me to insinuate, one day when I had accompanied him to Five Points to look for a messenger to the Cape, that perhaps he had Masonic leanings.

Gaspar became rather indignant, as we have seen already: no, he most certainly was not a Mason! A Catholic was what he was, even if he did skip mass more often than not and never went to confession or even prayed. If he could have his way, though, there would be no more convents, no more friars, and no more boys studying for the priesthood, except for those who wanted, of their own accord, to go into the seminary without being influenced by the excessive piety of their mothers or the cunning tricks of foreign monks.

Yes, Gaspar's Catholicism was rather peculiar. Such

opinions, however, were not held exclusively by João Gaspar da Rocha Wanderley, in whom there may have been secretly and subtly preserved—who can say?—a tradition of Protestant rationalism handed down to him by remote Dutch ancestors. His attitude was shared by many other Brazilians at that time. Gaspar himself reminded me of several imperial barons, and even viscounts, who thought as he did. He might have claimed, for that matter, that the Emperor himself thought as he did—or rather that he thought like the Emperor, Dom Pedro II.

12

IT WAS professional interest in the matter which led me to return, in a subsequent conversation with João Gaspar, to his curious way of adhering to the Catholic faith, and to try to learn more about his opinions regarding Freemasonry, Dom Vital, and the Bishops' Question [1]—all of which were still so fresh in Brazilian memory when José Maria was born that he was almost named Vital Maria. In the end it was decided that he should be called José, after his father from Pará, and Maria, in honor of both the Holy Virgin and Dom Vital—Vital Maria.

It was fortunate for me that I did speak to João Gaspar again on this subject, for our conversation enlightened me regarding several formerly obscure aspects of the struggle in Brazil between Catholicism, with its many followers, and Freemasonry, with its few. It was a struggle in which for some time the few held the advantage over the many because the few were well organized, while the many were notoriously disunited. Then, too, the few were in those days the ostensible or disguised owners of practically the whole of the Brazilian press, and they made astute use of caricature, through their excellent cartoonists (*One of whom, a mulatto named Vera Cruz, I met when I was a boy and he was already an old man*) as a

[1] The arrest and imprisonment of the Bishops of Olinda and Pará in 1875. (See footnote on Dom Vital, page 22.)

weapon with which to demoralize the Church and religion itself. Although the newspapers which served the interests of the Masons repeatedly called the priests and bishops *charlatans, priestlings, laughable pedagogues, swindlers, and sycophants,* as though every anticlerical scribbler had been ordered to use identical epithets against the enemy, their principal and most effective weapon against those *sycophants,* in a Brazil in which the general public has always taken delightedly to campaigns of ridicule, even against its most sacred institutions, was precisely that: ridicule, caricature, anecdote. *The old cartoonist whom I have already mentioned, who was employed by a journal aptly called* O Diabo a Quatro,[2] *told me that the intellectuals—the doctors, as he called them—who edited the famous anticlerical review took the greatest pains to supply him with ideas for his cartoons, and that one of them regularly provided him with rough sketches. Meanwhile, very few of the Catholic partisans had the courage to declare plainly that they were Apostolic Roman Catholics. Many preferred to call themselves liberals first and Catholics second, and their faint-heartedness contaminated bishops and even the Internuncio in Rio de Janeiro. The latter was an intimate of Viscount Rio Branco,[3] to whom he permitted the patri-*

[2] A colloquial phrase meaning "tumult," "bedlam," "the devil to pay."

[3] José Maria da Silva Paranhos, Viscount Rio Branco (1819–80), was one of the key figures of the Empire under the reign of Dom Pedro II. Five times a minister of state, and

archal privilege of a private chapel in his house, where regular masses were said. Even among the unequivocally Catholic, no one thought worthy of the Church the use of militant caricature as a counteroffensive, or aggressive, systematic ridicule of the Masons, or any reference to the weak points (there were some) in the character of Viscount Rio Branco, or, indeed, the use of any unconventional polemical technique whatever against the aggressive, unscrupulous enemy.

So great, nevertheless, was the moral strength of Dom Vital that when the whole campaign of ridicule against the Church and the clergy was at its virulent height, the young prelate, with the black beard that to João Gaspar always looked more like the beard of a sugar planter than that of a Penha friar, *went on foot through the streets and squares of Recife, in the midst of the boiling Masonic struggle. . . . And when mass was over, excited crowds would pour out of the churches and rush to kiss his ring.* With his own eyes João Gaspar had seen not only women but men too kneel to the ground to kiss the amethyst on the Capuchin's finger. It did not seem astonishing to him that such a thing could happen. According to Dona Sinhá's brothers, Dom Vital, who had been brought up on a

---

president of the longest-lasting Cabinet (1871–5) of the monarchical regime, the viscount was responsible for the "Law of the Free Womb," which envisaged the gradual extinction of slavery in Brazil. Rio Branco, a Masonic Grand Master, began his political career as a member of the Liberal Party, but he later became an outstanding Conservative leader.

Pernambuco plantation and been born in a place called
Pedra de Fogo,[4] was as stony and adamant in some ways
as he was fiery in others. No insignificant scribbler from
O Diabo a Quatro could prevent him from being stonily
unyielding in will and fiery in action. The figure of
speech is João Gaspar's, not mine. Never speaking except
in a drawl, always substituting *l* for *r*, the old fellow did
allow himself these occasional outbursts of something
very like eloquence—an eloquence that he himself
seemed to savor, as though elementary words like "stone"
and "fire" became vivid and tangible on his verbal palate.
The latter was, perhaps, very like his fleshly palate: fond
of marrow bone—which Dudu always saved for him—
and hot-pepper sauce.

João Gaspar provided me with a curious bit of information which I found, upon sifting through authentic contemporary documents, to be true: at the height of the
Masons' war against Dom Vital, the active members of
the Masonic lodges in Recife—the most aggressive in the
country in their war against the bishops—*numbered only
572, to whom might be added a mere 319 unaffiliated
and 14 honorary members.* And this in a Catholic population, in Recife in 1870, of 100,000 souls! How can
one account for the fact that so few could openly defy so
many priests, so many monks, so many Catholics? When
I discussed this point with João Gaspar, he pointed out
that the Masons, besides having the courage of their convictions—unlike many Catholics, including some of the

4 Literally, Rock of Fire.

priests, who played into the hands of the Masonic jour-
nalists by feeling ashamed of their religion and ashamed
not to align themselves with the "Progress of the Century," the celebrated "Century of Enlightenment"—were
busy carrying on what Gaspar called "termites' work."
*The priests who were partisans of Dom Vital might whis-
per militant secret orders into the ears of pious women to
influence their minds and their children's and, indirectly,
those of their husbands (even though the latter might
never go to mass or confession or even set foot in church
except for baptisms, weddings, and funeral services).
The Masons, however, carried on their insidious work
surreptitiously among the young men, the government
employees, the very ministers of the Empire, not so much
by initiating them into the secrets of the lodges as by
attracting their support, as "intelligent Brazilians," to
what they called the cause of liberalism, rationalism, and
progressiveness; the only cause that was worthy of enlightened men. This cause they described as incompatible
with the Church and the clergy, who were obedient to the
Pope and directed by a pack of reactionary Italian priests
in Rome. Already endangered even in newly liberal Italy,
which was rising up against her, the Church of Rome was
fighting—so said the Brazilian anticlericals—to keep the
Light of the Century from spreading its rays to backward
countries like the Empire of Brazil, which, by the way, no
longer had any business being an empire at all, even in
the British sense. This last argument seems to have man-
ifested itself in certain attitudes of the Emperor, Pedro II,*

who was himself a liberal rationalist, although not really a progressive: Baron Mauá's impetuous enthusiasm for material progress rather alarmed the Emperor. Since Dom Pedro lacked the manly will power and forcefulness of a Dom Vital—a will power, according to João Gaspar, *which resembled stone in its imperviousness to modern corruption and a forcefulness which was* (to resort once more to João Gaspar's figure of speech) *like fire in its ardent activity against the enemies of the Church—he all but hid his Catholic Emperor's crown from the cartoonists and the papo de tucano* [5] *which he wore at ceremonies of state from the beer-hall Bohemians of Rio de Janeiro and the self-important law students of São Paulo and Recife. All of the foregoing serves to illustrate the Emperor's adherence to "liberalism"—the adherence of an emperor who lacked the moral fiber to assume before Brazil any attitude that differed from that of the routine-loving clericalists on the one hand and that of the rabid anticlericals on the other. And so he yielded to the liberalism which had been built up into an irresistible wave by a handful of active Masons and to the rationalism with which they opposed, not Protestant Christianity (which was no doubt English in origin, as was Masonic policy in general), with which they intended to replace Catholicism in Brazil, but the Apostolic Roman Catholic Church. It was the Church, built on rock—"And on this rock I*

---

[5] A green cowl with yellow toucan feathers which was draped over the shoulders of the Brazilian Emperor at his coronation and on other solemn occasions.

shall *found my Church, etc."—and made,* as João Gaspar said when referring to Dom Vital, of fire—*the fire of that martial spirit which defied Protestant Germany and England and rationalistic France, and which tore from the grasp of England, so insular even in its Christianity, souls like that of the very Anglo-Saxon Manning and spirits of more than Oxonian genius like that of Newman —which was the supreme enemy to be destroyed by the liberals, acting through the Masons. At that time the Freemasons claimed that they, and no one else in Brazil, represented Liberalism, Rationalism, Christianity freed from superstition, and Progress: Progress, above all.*

*According to the Masonic press of Brazil in the early 1870's, the Masons were "the true disciples of the Martyr of Golgotha," while Catholics who were loyal to Rome and the Pope were nothing but "dark emissaries of the Curia, true pharisees." It was proclaimed in the contemporary Masonic press, and taken up in more than one newspaper, that Masonry was "a great temple, as was the city of Rome in days of yore, which shelters all gods alike. And all gods are but one: our heavenly Father." And, con-*tinuing in an ingenious vein of bamboozling metaphor: *"Masons lend their whole-hearted support to equality, liberty, and universal fraternity, the sublime unity whence true religion flows, for in it are revealed the persons of the Father, Son and Holy Ghost, under which was founded the religion of the one true God."* And again: *"If the banner raised aloft by the revolution of the nineteenth century has for its motto the word 'revolution,' it is as* *clear as daylight that that reform is aimed at the Church of Rome alone. It is only a question of time: the annihilation of the ancient Church will come to pass."* Let the priests prepare themselves to be annihilated—those priests who *"while saying mass regale their maws and gullets with white wine provided for them out of the pockets of pious hypocrites."*

All of the foregoing is rhetoric printed in Masonic newspapers at the time of Dom Vital's struggles. I copied these and other extracts from an old book of clippings I found in the home of an elderly enthusiast of Freemasonry, an enemy of Dom Vital who had, like Dona Sinhá, resided in São José for many years.

Such outspoken expressions of anti-Catholicism on the part of the Masonic lodges in Brazil were not systematically printed in the press under the Empire until the 1870's. Before that time the Masons had used other words and other methods. They had even pretended to be allies of the Church in order to win the confidence of priests who, if they were naïve, were nonetheless useful to the Masons by permitting themselves to be included among the members of a society avowedly devoted to the innocent practice of Christian charity. Dom Vital recorded these facts in one of his essays, copies of which are rarely seen today. I found this one in the jacarandá bookcase of that same elderly gentlemen of whom I have spoken, who allowed me to copy whatever interested me from his books and papers: *"Before 1872, Freemasonry in Brazil remained secret, giving no hint of its malevo-*

*lence toward the Catholic faith. It went so far as to intro-
duce itself, under the cloak of religion, into the bosom of
the clergy in the seminaries, convents, canonical societies, and religious fraternities. But no sooner did it behold
its Grand Master [6] at the head of the national government
than, finding itself armed for the struggle, it judged that
the time had come to unmask itself and attack the
Church with visor raised. . . ."*

Assured of protection in high places, the anticlerical
demagogues *committed shocking excesses such as the attack on the College of the Jesuits in Recife, causing the
death of a priest in that supremely cowardly assault; the
sabotage of a Catholic printing plant; and threats against
Dom Vital and the Bishop's Palace in Soledade. (Dom
Vital and Soledade Palace, which he had fashioned into a
fortress of revitalized, combative Catholicism, were a singular source of worry to Brazilian Masons.)
One participant in the street demonstrations against
the priests was José Mariano Carneiro da Cunha,[7] whose*
companion João Gaspar had been—not in street agitation
but in nocturnal revelries, when the two of them feasted
on Bohemian suppers with Mariano's coachman at the

---

[6] Viscount Rio Branco.

[7] José Mariano Carneiro da Cunha (1850–1912) was an influ-
ential Pernambuco politician—demagogical, abolitionist, and
anticlerical—who was elected a federal deputy several times
during the last years of the monarchy and the early years of
the Republic. He was a lawyer, journalist, and founder of the
Liberal Party newspaper, the *Província*.

open-air kiosks that stood next to the bridge in Recife. The young politician, always a great Bohemian in his younger days, would occasionally stop at one of these kiosks for sarapatel *and new wine.* Joaquim Nabuco, *who dined with José Mariano more than once at Carneiro da Cunha's house on the bank of the Capibaribe River in Poço de Panela,* could not sympathize with his friend's excesses. He was Mariano's friend, but only up to a point. On one occasion, when Nabuco was booed by a Recife crowd, João Gaspar learned (probably from Mariano's coachman) *that it had been Carneiro da Cunha who had inflamed the crowd against Nabuco.* The two men had much in common. Both were sugar-plantation aristocrats, and both had deserted their own class. Both had renounced some of their privileges as men of the ruling caste to agitate in the streets against the large property- and slave-owners, the great barons of the Imperial cane fields and coffee plantations, whom they thought hopelessly feudal. But each acted according to his own lights. João Gaspar was acquainted with both; and although he had been Mariano's comrade, he said to me more than once that he had recognized in Nabuco a greatness lacking in the good José Mariano.

In the course of my conversations with João Gaspar about the "religious question," of which he had been a witness in his youth, I never failed to notice that although anticlerical and at the same time Catholic in his own unique, almost Protestant way, the man admired Dom Vital. Not that he considered him the holy Catholic, the martyr of the Faith, the hero of the Church that the bishop was to Dona Sinhá, who had passed on to her son her own adoration for the Capuchin whom João Gaspar had dubbed "a Goiana [Pernambuco] amarelo." [8] No, it was rather that Gaspar, who was not a "Goiana amarelo" but a full-blooded Wanderley from Serinhaém, felt akin to Vital Maria Gonçalves de Oliveira through virtues which seemed to him to exemplify the true caboclo—who, according to Gaspar's criteria as to who deserved to be called a caboclo, did not necessarily have Indian blood in his veins. What made a Brazilian a caboclo was his loyalty to himself and to Brazil, the firmness of his convictions and sentiments, his capacity to hold out against passing fads, and his courage in opposing the powerful men of his time—all in a very Brazilian way. The Italian priests, according to Gaspar (who had mistrusted Italian priests from the very beginning), had never succeeded, for all their pretense of speaking for the Pope and their mingling of what Dona Sinhá's brother called their "foxy Italian" with Church Latin, in making Dom Vital bend his will to that of the Emperor and the president of the Council, Viscount Rio Branco, who was also the Supreme Head of the Masonic Order in Brazil. When speaking of

[8] In northeastern Brazil the word *amarelo* (or *amarelinho*) describes a person with the yellowish pallor imparted by malaria or a tropical climate. In a wider sense, the amarelinho, even when slight and of an apparently frail constitution, is idealized in the popular Brazilian mind as superior to foreigners of twice his size in tenacity, intelligence, and sexual prowess.

"old Italian foxes," João Gaspar was referring particularly to the *Internuncio, Monsignor Sanguigni, who, in order to please the all-powerful viscount, actually went to the extreme of trying to suborn the Bishop of Olinda, with the permission of the imperial Court, by promising him a large sum of money on condition that the Capuchin leave Soledade Palace and absent himself from the diocese. The bishop's reaction to this attempt at bribery was less characteristic of a Capuchin, perhaps, than of one of those caboclos who had resisted the seventh-century Dutch invaders, thus disobeying the King the better to serve him—that is, to serve a king who was cowed in the face of the enemy. Dom Vital disobeyed the Pope in order to serve him; in order to serve the Pope, and not a cowardly pope surrounded in Rome by cowardly diplomat-priests and represented in Rio de Janeiro by a Nuncio who was cowed by the Masonic overlords of the imperial government. That is the long and the short of it—the sad and simple truth. The "religious question" in Brazil was accompanied by an access of cowardice. The cowardice of the diplomat-priests maintained by Rome itself in the Nunciate in Rio de Janeiro was compounded by the cowardice of numerous Brazilian Catholics who had been thrown off balance by the efficient organization of a few Masons, who virtually controlled the government in the person of Viscount Rio Branco.*

Dom Antônio Macedo Costa, Bishop of Pará and a staunch ally of Dom Vital in his fight against the Masons entrenched in the highest posts of the Imperial govern-

ment, clearly recognized the problem when he stated that there were in Brazil at that time "statesmen who were upright, honest, conscientious, but powerless." Such statesmen became lax, yielded power too easily, and temporized to excess. The government was then in the hands of such men as these, who were incapable of "keeping 'order,'" which the government itself turned into "disorder" by permitting demagogic excesses which were, without a doubt, encouraged by the Masons, such as the attacks in Recife on a Jesuit school and a Catholic printing press, which ended, as has been recorded here, in the killing of a priest by the aggressors. When such excesses were permitted, it seemed to the Bishop of Pará that there was no longer any "government in the true sense of the word." Dom Antônio, falling into an error of exaggeration himself and forgetting the cowardice of the Apostolic Nuncio, Monsignor Domingos Sanguigni, spoke of "the flaccid, undynamic constitution of our race." But what was the brave, resolute Vital if not a specimen of that race, and such a characteristic specimen of its deceptive weakness, which is more apparent than real, that during his novitiate in Versailles and Perpignan, his superiors were convinced that he would not be able to withstand the rigors of the European winter and the Franciscan regimen? It was true that at that time he had "a very frail and delicate constitution." For long months the pale young man—who was "naturally delicate," in the words of a contemporary, and unaccustomed to hardship, for he was the son of a gentlewoman who had brought him up surrounded by tenderness and every comfort—suffered "serious infirmities" in Europe "with no fire, no cozy bed, no comfort whatever." When he became gravely ill while a seminary student in France, the pale little Brazilian valiantly endured "the most violent pain," according to the testimony of one of his superiors. One could see that "his face was contorted with pain, but no cry or exclamation ever escaped from his lips," so great was the self-control of the frail Brazilian who, because of his many illnesses, which were those of a tropical adolescent in a cold climate, was given up by the French doctors as a hopeless case. The fact was that the French doctors, with all their learning, knew nothing of the bodily resistance, recuperative powers, and strength of mind of Brazilian amarelinhos in general and of that little "Goiana amarelinho" in particular. Thus, when the physicians told their neophyte-patient that he would have to choose between certain death and leaving the order and returning to Brazil, the amarelinho did not hesitate for an instant: he chose to be loyal to the rule of the order he had embraced, disregarding his own life in so doing.

Vital Maria survived. Perhaps God had been testing him. It did not take him long to regain the health he had temporarily lost, to adapt himself to the rigors of the European winter and the harsh rule of the Franciscan monastery. Once Vital Maria had recovered, it was apparent that he was, according to a witness of the time, "handsome of face"; and that in his eyes and "in all his ways" there was a "striking virginal candor," which did not pre-

vent him from being "gay and lively, while at the same time reserved and calm." Furthermore, he combined what to his superiors seemed "a gentleman's urbanity" (which was doubtless part of his heritage as the son of a Pernambuco plantation owner) with an ascetic austerity, and even, according to another eyewitness, "a poet's tenderness" with "the rigorous logic of a mathematician."

Such was the friar who, having returned to Brazil, was consecrated Bishop of Olinda at the age of twenty-six. "His Majesty, the Emperor of Brazil," he wrote to Pope Pius IX on October 8, 1871, "has deigned to call me, with no merit whatever on my part, insignificant and obscure as I am, to the Cathedral Church of Olinda." And the letter concluded, dramatically and humbly: "My poor terrified soul clamors for your most pious clemency: Oh, Father, if it be possible, let this cup pass from me!"

Pius IX was pleased by the choice of the twenty-six-year-old Capuchin as Bishop of Olinda. A bishop he was forthwith ordained—a bishop resolved to undertake the whole difficult task of revitalizing the customs of the clergy and the attitude of the Church in Brazil in the second half of the nineteenth century, a revolutionary bishop. In the eyes of superficial men he was a conservative and the Masons were revolutionaries. In reality, it was the pupil of the Versailles priests who brought the fire of revolution from neo-Catholic France to Brazil. The Masons were in favor of the status quo: *in favor of priests who were not so much priests as bureaucrats at the service of the Empire; not so much priests as politicians of the ilk of Monsignor Pinto de Campos; priests who lived openly with concubines; priests with sons whom they called "nephews" or "godsons"; unworthy priests and friars. An Englishman noted the following piece of information, which he obtained from a trustworthy Brazilian witness: "The priesthood in this country is superlatively corrupt." He went on to cite examples: the tragic one of a woman found dead in St. Anthony's Monastery in Rio de Janeiro, who had died of abuses inflicted on her by the monks, one of whom had smuggled her in dressed in a Franciscan habit; and that of a lady, also from Rio, who had been just as tragically debauched by one of the Italian Capuchins who had come to Brazil with Empress Teresa Cristina. The Italians added to the wave of clerical corruption, already widespread enough among the native priests and friars, very few of whom were virgins or even chaste. Nearly all had their women—colored women, as often as not.*

Many such priests were Masons, or liberals, or nationalists. Being Masons gave them the paradoxical sensation of being priests and anticlericalists at the same time. With half of their energies they served Rome, and with the other half worked against Rome. This latter characteristic won for them the sympathy of the liberal politicians, with whom they held two or three points of view in common. Both felt that it was their charity that made them Christians, and that charity was the core of Christianity. Both felt, too, that their dislike of foreigners made them Brazilian: there were priests who tended to be more nationalistic than they were Catholic. This had been true ever since the struggle for independence, so ardently espoused by the Masons. From that time on, the fact that the Church was united to the state led many Brazilian priests to think of themselves as state functionaries rather as servants of the Church, which was directed from Rome by the Pope.

It was only natural that priests of this stamp should see in Dom Vital a revolutionary intruder, come to lay about him with his bishop's scepter, who was bent on radically altering habits of long and comfortable standing among the priests, clerical irregularities tacitly accepted by Brazilian society, and alliances long since established between many of the native priests and the patriarchal institution of the family—an institution more characteristic of Brazil in the nineteenth century than the institution of monarchy itself, and one to which the Catholic religion had conformed by subsiding into a form of religious observance that was more domestic than ecclesiastical. It was against such abuses, which affronted orthodox Catholicism, that Dom Vital rose up in arms with the support of friars, nuns, and priests—foreigners as well as Brazilians—who felt as he did, or who had caught his revolutionary fervor and thrown off their conservative apathy. These religious became revolutionaries, cutting their ties with the Masons. They helped bring about the beginnings of a Catholic reformation in Brazil which was to continue throughout the Republican period, gaining in vigor after the separation of church and state.

Let no one today, after the lapse of almost a century, be deceived into thinking that the beginning of this reformation was easy. On the contrary: it was extremely difficult. The movement had its martyr, and that martyr was Friar Vital Maria, the Capuchin who had been born—symbolically, it seemed—in Pedra de Fogo. Brazilian Catholicism was rebuilt on that Rock. On that Rock and on that Fire, as Gaspar would have said; *but only with the sacrifice of the Capuchin who had been brought up in Brazil by his aristocratic mother as carefully as though he had been a girl, but who had been tempered in France by hard winters and an even harder Franciscan rule.*

Dom Vital was defeated—Catholicism was defeated—in the first battle. That battle was won by the Masons, who had cast dust in the eyes of the government, officially Catholic though it was; by the political Masons, who dominated most of the Brazilian press, encouraged the demagogues, and even protected the street agitators. "Whoever controls the press in this country," *the Bishop of Pará wrote in* 1888 *in a retrospective study of the Bishops' Question,* "and can surround himself with a pack of mediocre, wordy, restless, ambitious men to encourage tumult and disorder in the streets and public squares, will soon be strong enough to paralyze any action the government may take, and will, in fact, eventually have the government on his side."

The Brazilian press, at the time the conflict was being waged between an organized, wealthy minority (which was probably financed in part from sources outside the country) and the Catholics, who, although vastly in the majority, were totally disorganized, would make an interesting study. Institutions very characteristic of Brazil and its press were then at the height of their popularity: the "independent articles," the signed or unsigned "contributions," and the "figureheads." The figurehead was an individual paid to sign his name to insulting attacks on respectable people, written by defamers who lacked the courage to make their identity known to the public. Dom Vital, the priests who were most faithful to the Church, and even the Catholic religion itself were the victims of printed attacks signed by figureheads of this sort—poor devils, often enough without the money to pay for their own funerals, who were willing to submit to any indignity for cash.

In the house of that same former Mason already referred to, I leafed through some newspapers published at the time of Dom Vital's struggle against the Masons and found them extremely interesting. One—the *Diário do Grão-Pará,* published in Belém—had printed a letter from a certain Canon Sebastião Borges de Castilhos, in which the prelate railed with such brazen insolence against his bishop that the Masonic collector of press clippings had written in blue pencil in the margin of this "letter to the public": "Why doesn't the Canon drink tea made from . . . [illegible—probably some soothing herb]?"

13

THE FACT that Dona Sinhá's son had been born only a few years after the arrest of the bishops of Pará and Olinda explains much of the zeal with which the devout plantation aristocrat prepared that son, from the day the boon she implored of the Blessed Virgin Mary was granted, for a life of service to Mary and the Church of Rome. She had almost named him Vital Maria in honor of the "Martyr-Bishop." *Catholic Brazil had breathlessly accompanied the martyrdom of the Bishop of Olinda: his imprisonment, together with the Bishop of Pará, on the Isle of Cobras and the dramatic unexpectedness of his gesture in donning his bishop's robes and investing himself with all the emblems, all the lace, all the liturgical purples of his office before leaving Soledade Palace as a prisoner of the Government of His Imperial Majesty. As the official coach rolled through the streets of Recife, bearing away the bishop who was so eminently a man of God, Catholic Recife was beside itself with emotion. Vital Maria: no other name was so deeply impressed on the imagination of Catholic Brazil in the 1870's. For every orthodox Catholic, those years were a time of exaltation of the name of Mary: Mary Most Holy! Mary Most Blessed! Mary Most Pure!*

A Brazilian Tale

An intensely marianistic spirit pervaded Brazil at that time, among the most orthodox of Catholics and the most ardent devotees of Christian folklore. It was a time of fervent adoration of the Mother of God, the Woman and Mother, and the Brazilian mother, an adoration that was also reflected in the emphasis given to the duties of Brazilian mothers toward the Church. It would no longer suffice for them to give just any child to the Church as a priest, a monk, or a nun, as had formerly been common practice, often for reasons having nothing to do with religion. Mothers now had a moral obligation to dedicate their most talented sons and daughters to the service of religion. Each loving mother should bring up that chosen son or daughter with the utmost care, so that his or her virtue as a priest or a nun would resemble that of the holiest saints. Implicit in the cult of Mary, the Virgin Mother, was the restoration of another, anti-Brazilian cult: that of virginity.

Dona Sinhá herself had thought more than once of taking a nun's vows and, consequently, remaining a virgin. At one time she had almost obtained her wish, which was also that of her mother. It was not, however, the wish of the elderly master of Olindeta, who liked the bachelor of law from Pará who had begun to court Sinhá when she was still a young girl. Highly recommended to the girl's family by a sugar merchant married to a lady from one of the first families of Pará, he had begun by cultivating Sinhá's parents rather than Sinhá herself.

The paraense was, in the end, successful in his suit.

Once Sinhá had accepted him, the wedding was arranged without much delay. The couple was married, and the young husband, who was employed in a Recife law office, decided to settle down for good in his wife's native state. Since the Olindeta Wanderleys had a fine, roomy house on the Rua do Alecrim, which at that time was an aristocratic street where even barons lived, the house was given to the bride.

Sinhá brought with her as personal servants from Olindeta to the Rua do Alecrim the maid and the little houseboy who have already appeared in these pages. Matters went along smoothly enough between husband and wife. Sinhá was still as devoted as ever to the Church, the saints, and the Virgin Mary, and very eager to have a son who would be as devoted to the Virgin as she was; while the young lawyer was very bureaucratic, very dull, and very devoted—when his normal obligations permitted it —not to the saints, but to his Amazonian plants, to which he attributed so many miraculous healing virtues that it was no exaggeration to say that the plants meant as much to him as the saints did to Dona Sinhá.

No doubt that was why he did not become as excited as his wife over the Affair of the Bishops. His point of view was, it is true, as impeccably Catholic as Dona Sinhá's: he was on the side of Dom Vital and the Church and against the Masons and anticlericalists, but without enthusiasm or fire. The Amazonian tropics had given their son but one passion: the cultivation of the region's plants, which few people had studied as thoroughly as he. He was familiar with the characteristics of each of them. Such exaggerated confidence did he have in the healing and restorative qualities of his plants, and in their power to bring back the luster to a sick man's hair and the color to his cheeks, that he was convinced that a doctor who had been graduated in Bahia or Rio de Janeiro or Europe was an excrescence on the face of Brazil. All that Brazilians had to know about medicine was what the Amazon caboclos knew. It was probably this caboclo stubbornness which put the paraense in the good graces of the Olindeta Wanderleys, all of whom were inclined, despite their own Nordic traits, which were intermingled with very few drops of Indian blood, to think of themselves as part Indian and all Brazilian. Combining his adoration of Amazonian plants with his wife's adoration of the Church and Dom Vital, it occurred to him, on being introduced one day to the Bishop of Olinda when the Bishops' Question was at boiling point, to prescribe for the prelate a certain herb from Pará to make his black beard gleam and another that would impart a rosier color to the Bishop's dark pallor, which was, after all, his normal hue as a son of the tropics, not the pallor of a sick man.

Sinhá's husband agreed to her wish that their son be named José, after him, and Maria, in honor of the most holy Virgin and—as has already been noted—in honor of Dom Vital Maria. Thus it came about that José Maria was born under the sign of Dom Vital. In her innermost heart Dona Sinhá had no greater desire than that her son, who had become to her an object of far greater tenderness than any she had ever felt for her husband, should be another Dom Vital: just such a priest, just such a monk, just such a man of religion as Vital. José Maria would lead a chaste and virtuous life. His soul would belong to God alone and his body to the Church—and he would never love any woman but his mother, with the sole exception of the Mother Most Holy, Mary Immaculate, Mary Most Blessed.

When, on one of those wet, dreary days on which the city of Recife seems to be longing to return to its Dutch Calvinist past, the paraense died of convulsions against which all the Amazonian plants, the medical knowledge of the Recife doctors, and the sincere prayers of the young wife were equally unavailing, Dona Sinhá felt well up in her again the old longing to belong more to God than to the world. Of course she had her son, for whose sake she would have to go on with the daily round of domestic tasks. But what if that son should some day wish to emulate his mother in devotion to the Virgin Mary? From that day on, Dona Sinhá devoted herself intensely to one thing only: to molding her son into a true child of the Holy Virgin, consecrated exclusively to Her service. Perhaps he would be a new Dom Vital Maria. Dom José Maria . . . Friar José Maria . . . Father José Maria. Soon the little boy's illness, her promise to the Virgin, and the little invalid's recovery dramatically heightened his mother's desire that he become a priest.

When her son fell gravely ill, Dona Sinhá spoke aloud the solemn promise that she had long before made to the

Virgin Mary in her heart: if José Maria recovered, he would become a priest. If he regained his health, he would wear white and blue, the colors of virginity, until the day he donned his cassock, and he would walk in every religious procession dressed as a priest.

The behavior imposed by Sinhá on her small son served to widen the gulf of incomprehension which had divided her from her brother João Gaspar since early childhood. Not that they had not loved each other as children; they had. But neither of them had ever really understood the other. João Gaspar could never accustom himself to certain subtle nuances in the behavior of his sister, who, having received a better education than he, had at the same time become more devoutly religious— more superstitious, João Gaspar would have said. Gaspar thought of himself as a man free from superstition. He had stopped believing in werewolves very early, and his Catholicism had never been strictly that of the Church, being rather a Catholicism filtered through the mind of a man who was a Protestant without knowing it. It will do no harm to remind ourselves once again that Gaspar's ancestor of the same name, who had come from Reformed Holland to Catholic Brazil and become a Catholic convert after living there for some time, had passed down to his descendants something in his nature which was immutably Protestant. This, of course, is sheer speculation, in which we have already indulged when discussing João Gaspar, and it is simply repeated here for what it is worth.

The fact was that while José Maria was growing up, he was influenced far more by his mother than by any advice or suggestions broached by his uncle, who had become a vague substitute for his dead father. José Maria's own character—that of a boy with a bit of the girl in him— had predisposed him in that direction. When his mother stopped cutting his baby hair, allowing it to grow as long as that of a girl so that it could later adorn the image of Mary's son, José Maria accepted his mother's decision without a sign of protest, seemingly thinking of himself as part girl. Perhaps he had been persuaded by his mother that it was more important to serve the Virgin Mary and her Blessed Son than to look like the other boys he knew, who had been differentiated early and emphatically, as all boys are in Brazil, from girl children. Someone did protest, however: João Gaspar. His protests were loud and angry. He tried to form a secret alliance between uncle and nephew against his nephew's mother; against both mothers, the earthly and the heavenly; against the child's being swallowed up by his two mothers —in short, against Dona Sinhá and the Blessed Mary herself. He might have saved his breath. While manifesting no fervor or enthusiasm for the demands Dona Sinhá was making on him, José Maria, who resembled in this his Pará father rather than his Pernambuco mother, submitted to them discreetly and tenderly. He gradually, docilely grew to be as much a child of the Virgin Mary as he was a child of Dona Sinhá. He knew nothing of any influence that his dead father might have had over him, and he gently thwarted every attempt on the part of his rustic, masculine uncle to become a father-substitute for his nephew or to take the place of the old grandfather who had at one time been almost another father to José Maria, but of whom the boy had almost no recollection.

José Maria was never to be ordained. He almost became a priest, but not quite. Nevertheless, he was almost universally accorded the respect due a priest after he had been a short time in the seminary. He was so grave and judicious that people would ask for his blessing while he was still only an adolescent seminarian—a vivid contrast indeed to the days when some of the more irreverent street urchins in São José could never see him go by without shouting "Missy!"

It was not only the boys in the streets. We know already that in school José Maria was sometimes so teased and insulted by children of his own class, with their shouts of "Missy," that his resolution could not hold out against such rudeness. There were times when he shed tears and even rebelled against his mother. He may even, in his secret heart, have stopped wanting to be so very much a son of Dona Sinhá.

It was an impossible wish. Dona Sinhá's son he was and would remain for the rest of his life—a son who was almost a daughter, affectionate as only daughters usually are, at least ostensibly, toward their mothers.

Furthermore, although José Maria was temperate in his enthusiasms, a trait that reflected his father rather than his mother, he began to look more and more like

Dona Sinhá as time went on. He had his mother's delicate features, her smile, her gestures, even her walk, which was not entirely in harmony with his sex. His speech, too, resembled Dona Sinhá's, which was an odd mixture of the leisurely, at times disagreeably nasal Serinhaém Wanderley drawl with occasional odd accelerations of rhythm in certain phrases that she had learned from the French sisters. These nuns, whether they lived in Rio or Recife, possessed an un-Brazilian clarity of expression which did justice to the nuances in the pronunciation of certain words, as well as a light, agile intonation at certain moments and for certain effects. This trait has been absent, probably since colonial times, from the speech of well-educated Brazilian women—northerners and southerners alike—with a single exception: the emphatic speech of the half-Spanish gauchos living on the borders of Spanish America, which is the exact opposite of the usual slurred pronunciation of words that are attractive only when pronounced with a certain degree of vigor.

José Maria was not blond and fair-skinned like his mother. The blood of his paraense father had given to his skin the dark pallor of a northern Brazilian, a dark tinge that his ruddy-skinned, red-haired, yet determinedly caboclo uncle may well have envied. An anthropologist, given the opportunity to study the portrait of José Maria which Dona Sinhá kept in her sitting room, would have had no difficulty in identifying Nordic features in the adolescent face—beautiful Nordic features accentuated by a hint of the remotely tropical Brazilian caboclo. Such an anthropologist might have been inclined to agree with those Occidental artists who have for centuries drawn the inspiration for their figures of angels from Nordic rather than Mediterranean types.

Angels—the Scriptures speak of angels for whom it would be a terrible sin for mere men to nurture sexual desire under the fascination of their beauty, which is sometimes greater than that of women—angels who, according to some interpreters of the Bible, adopt forms like those of adolescents of yet indeterminate sex.

Something of this exquisitely angelic character— which I noticed years ago in some English adolescents, students at an Oxford that has hardly survived the changes forced upon it by the social realities of our time, either in its physical aspect or as an expression of an era of European civilization which no longer exists—seems to have been inherent in Dona Sinhá's son from childhood. The impression communicated by his portrait is unmistakable, and so is that which I received from the testimony gathered from people who had known him well: his mother, his uncle, the Capuchins who doubtless heard his confessions, and his former school and seminary classmates.

Things being as they were, José Maria's natural destiny was bound to be that of a priest whose vow of chastity was inspired by an attachment to his mother which stopped just short of mysticism, and by a love of the Blessed Virgin which went beyond it. He seemed almost biologically predestined for the permanent state of son

and virgin in which he ended his days. Not that José
Maria was never tormented by sex. His tropical adolescence undoubtedly did torment him, as it must have tormented the future Friar Vital Maria in Versailles. In all
probability it informed his childhood with that conscious-
ness of having sinned which the writer has attributed to
him—perhaps a little too arbitrarily—in an earlier chapter, drafted before the vague pre-José Maria, conjured up
out of psychological probabilities, had evolved into the
more tangible José Maria, re-creation of whom in later
chapters was accomplished more through detection—
that is, the unraveling of clues leading to an under-
standing of a developing personality—than through the
techniques used by those biographers who pass over such
clues when writing works of history or historical novels,
preferring to base their work on logical rather than psychological probabilities. It is best, however, not to inter-
rupt the flow of this narrative with discourses on methodology which will in due course be applied in recounting
this story of a boy who became a priest and who evidently
fulfilled, in so doing, a mystical longing on the part of his
mother which was in turn based on his own suitability
for such a destiny.

True, a malicious reader might, at this point—assum-
ing on a small scale the role of devil's advocate—insinuate that Dona Sinhá's son did not die a virgin but a
semi-virgin. He had, after all, been furiously and sensually kissed on the mouth—one of José Maria's former
schoolmates indiscreetly told me of having surprised this

idyllic scene—by his schoolboy protector Paulo Tavares:
the same Paulo Tavares who, perhaps in order to give
substance to a vague, idyllic dream and satisfy a confused craving for love which had no definite object, set
his heart on marrying Dona Sinhá after José Maria's
death. The fact that she was several years older than he
was to him an attraction rather than an obstacle.

I do not think that my hypothetical devil's advocate
will be able to make his arguments against the little
priest's virginity prevail. My opinion is supported by the
testimony of another former pupil in old Miranda's
school. Although still a child when the petty scandal took
place, he had known both Paulo and José Maria, and he
affirmed that neither of the two was depraved. Reflecting
on the event long afterward, he concluded that what had
happened was only a flare-up of loving friendship, which
was probably more pronounced on the part of the older
boy than on that of the younger. There was little doubt
that it had been a purely lyrical overflowing of love, and
that no erotic act had resulted from it. It was as though
the angelic aura that surrounded José Maria had shielded
his body and soul from any aggression that could seriously have endangered the virginity of the one and the
purity of the other.

José Maria had been involved in another scandal, according to old Miranda's former pupil—a more shocking
occurrence than the kiss surprised by an indiscreet ob-
server, who had immediately spread the news all over the
school. No one, however, believed that José Maria had

sunk to the level of those overly pretty schoolboys who, besieged by stronger, more worldly companions, eventually agree to partake of erotic adventures in which the victim of aggression mimics the role of a woman and the stronger boy that of a man. No, the second scandal was of a different sort.

One day a big boy, almost a full-grown youth, shouted for everyone to hear that he did not think Missy was a virgin. Spewing forth the vilest indecencies in the presence of schoolboys of tender age, he swore that he would enjoy Dona Sinhá's son as a man enjoys a woman.

Before the reckless words had cooled in the air, another husky youth rose up in Missy's defense. That Missy was too prim and prissy he would not deny; and if he were Missy's brother he would make him change his ways and play I spy and puss-in-the-corner with the other boys instead of moping in corners during recess. But no one was going to insult Missy in his presence. It was as though the offender had insulted a brother of Missy's champion, and he was to go and apologize immediately to the boy he had slandered so vilely. At first the offending youth tried to pass off the incident as a joke; but then, giving in to the other boy, he admitted that he had gone too far and finally apologized to Missy, who only then learned what happened in his and Paulo's absence.

This incident shows that Missy was looked down upon because of his excessively refined manners, which were scorned by most of his schoolmates. It was not that the nickname "Missy," by which he was known to everyone in

Miranda's school, implied that his companions thought that his admittedly exaggerated friendship for Paulo meant that the two were linked in lechery, as sometimes happens in boarding schools and even in day schools. What "Missy" really expressed, on the lips of his school-fellows, was the disdain nearly all of them felt for José Maria's finicky ways: the almost girlish voice in which he recited his lessons; his excessive attachment to Dona Sinhá; his devotion—also considered excessive by the other boys—to the Virgin Mary, to whose image in the school oratory he sometimes took flowers, probably more out of obedience to his mother's wishes than from any initiative of his own. Among English schoolboys, José Maria would have been an "aesthete" in contrast to the "athletes." In no sense was he a degraded, passive peder-ast who would consent to serve as a woman for the oth-ers. Unimpeachable testimony assures us of that. We can therefore assert that in this particular at least, José Maria never dishonored his station as a son destined by his mother for the service of the Church, a station which must have sublimated whatever erotic desires had in-duced him to receive the kisses of his masculine friend, whom he identified with the saint of his preference, after the Virgin Mary: St. Louis Gonzaga.

We already know that José Maria's life in the seminary was that of an adolescent whose attention was concen-trated on his studies and religious duties—which were clothed for him with aesthetic charm—rather than on school itself, much less on games or sports.

He rested from his reading by gazing at the ocean with the eyes of one who is disenchanted with life on earth. There is no doubt that excessive study contributed to his illness and that he was warned by the doctors who examined him—just as the future Dom Vital had been warned at the seminary in Versailles—to give up any thought of studying for the priesthood, and to seek a more healthful climate than that of Olinda. One of the doctors actually hinted that what José Maria urgently needed was a woman, that what was scourging his body was woman-hunger. The doctor's opinion reached the ears of João Gaspar and gave new encouragement to his old desire to have José Maria at his side on the black clay soil of Olinda. If he could not accompany his uncle on the rougher trails, he could at least help him with the less brutal tasks. He would be the new master of a great-house that was in danger of becoming the dominion of bastards; and Olindeta run by bastards was an Olindeta that repelled the Boer once removed who evidently lurked in João Gaspar, the descendant of Dutchmen.

José Maria ignored the advice of his doctors, just as Vital Maria, future Bishop of Olinda, had done before him, and chose to remain faithful to the Church and the priesthood, faithful to his vows of chastity and virginity. He went on with his studies and came very close to being ordained, close to becoming a priest.

Virginity was not the cause of his weakness. The real cause—according to the doctor who cared for José Maria best during his sickness—was the consumptive tendency inherited from his father. No syrup of pharmaceutical concoction could stem his illness, nor could any of his father's herbs from Pará: that chest sickness was unknown to the Indians. It was a European sickness. A change of air could do him no good, either. Dona Sinhá, having first taken her son to Tegipió, later went with him to Angelim, where she had been told that one of her tubercular Wanderley relatives had recovered his health. *It was also in Angelim, however, that Maria Raymunda Wanderley, a cousin of Dona Sinhá, had died after spitting blood.* Dona Sinhá had not known of this until she arrived in Angelim and saw Maria Raymunda's grave.

It was there in Angelim that José Maria too was destined to waste away, his great sad eyes seeming to long for the sea. He had been born close to the sea, had grown up within sight of it, and secretly had felt the spell of Iemanjá. He had studied in Olinda, watching the sea and sometimes wondering what lay beyond it.

There was no ocean near Angelim. The landscape, which resembled neither Olindeta nor Serinhaém nor Rio Formoso, no doubt made the little sick priest feel as though he was indeed far from home. Had any place, however, truly been his home, his own place, for which he could feel homesickness?

None, perhaps. The truth was that the black clay of Olindeta had never clung lovingly to the feet of the timid child. Nor had the sand of the beaches, nor the mud on the banks of the rivers in which other Josés, closer to the earth than he, caught fresh-water crabs, singing and telling dirty jokes. He had never truly belonged to any place.

The life of a priest undoubtedly had attracted José Maria in the end because it was something that loosened his ties with every place on earth, from the river-bank mud of Recife to the sticky black clay of Olindeta. The consumption seemed to sharpen his sensation of withdrawal from anything that might have tied him to the earth. He confessed as much to his mother, as though grateful to God for the consumption that was liberating him from yearnings that might have embittered the end of life on earth for one who was still so young.

Dona Sinhá told me that her son had passed away very gently, kissing her hand and asking her to kiss his forehead. As she did so, Dona Sinhá felt how hot and feverish it was—a testa calda, like Dom Vital's.

Very pale, but with the eyes, as Dona Sinhá recalled, of one who feels close to the Virgin Mary, José Maria had pressed Dona Sinhá's hand as though in recognition of what she too had suffered because of the children who had called him Missy and jeered at him for not being one of them. José Maria must already have felt homesick for Dona Sinhá at the moment of his death, and perhaps for Paulo too. But that longing was doubtless softened by the mystical certainty that he was about to meet the Blessed Virgin, whose name he bore and whose example he had tried to follow.

14

WHILE STILL on board the ship, Paulo saw, on the first
cutter approaching the English liner, the Republican
flag with its motto "Order and Progress." He had left Brazil under the banner of the Empire. After studying and
living in Europe for so many years, he sometimes had the
impression that he had forgotten half of his Portuguese.
Someone in the cutter shouted his name: Tavarès! Tavarès was what he was called in France. He hardly recognized his own name as he heard it shouted by relatives in
the cutter nearing the ship. In Paris he had not often
mingled with Brazilians—only with Frenchmen and,
above all, with Frenchwomen.

Now that his father was dead, he felt it his duty to be
near his widowed mother, who had written him a letter so
unhappy that it was more like an anguished appeal. Life
was empty to her, the Recife aristocrat wrote to her European son, without the familiar presence of her husband;
now that she could no longer hear him talk or clear his
throat; no longer had his company all day; no longer
heard the companionable sound of his black walking
boots or his felt carpet slippers as he shuffled about looking after his birds or wandered into the kitchen to taste
the guava jam cooking on the stove or the canjica while it

was still warm in the pan. Yes, Tavares had been the mildest and most peaceable of men.

Paulo knew from his mother's letters that the elder Tavares had spent most of his time at home after old age and sickness had forced him to retire from the sugar business, leaving the management of the firm almost entirely in the hands of his partner. He had always enjoyed raising birds in cages, but with his increased stoutness and leisure as a semi-invalid, the hobby had become an obsession. The house was full of bird cages, some of which he had made himself, with a painstaking slowness that was equaled only by that of his wife when she made lace for the images of the saints. Tavares had a bevy of canaries, cardinals, thrushes, even bellbirds, to take the place of his noisy son, who had been so mischievous as a child and so silently absent after he was grown.

Paulo knew very well that old Tavares had more than once regretted having agreed to let his only son study medicine in France instead of in Bahia, where the doctors knew just as much as the French. It must be confessed that once Paulo was in Europe, he had written to his parents infrequently. He had promised visits home which were always postponed, until his father and mother (or so he thought) had resigned themselves to his ungrateful absence while never ceasing to love him with the best and most Brazilian of loves, or hoping for his return long after his graduation, as though he were another Sebastian and had finally triumphed over the Frenchwomen instead of over the Moors. When the prodigal son returned home at last, he realized that his mother and father had both been convinced all along that it was no cold, impersonal goddess of wisdom who was keeping their son from them, but the semi-goddesses of the boulevards, the blondes who were even cleverer than mulatto women at the art of bewitching men.

It was sad that he should be going home to Recife too late to see his father wearing slippers on his plump, bare feet as though enjoying a holiday from boots, his slightly clumsy hands tending his fledglings with Franciscan tenderness. He had died two months before. Paulo knew that there awaited him a weeping mother who had lost a Juca she had no doubt thought eternal.

It was just as he had imagined. For hours and days he saw her burst into tears at the slightest provocation. Even the singing of the birds that old Tavares had raised, far from being a consolation to her, seemed to keep her sorrow brutally fresh in her mind. It was as though the beaks of that flock of birds, who probably missed the old man in their way, were cruelly pecking at the poor widow's wounds and opening them afresh each morning.

Paulo had returned from Europe on board an English vessel on a sunny Sunday, which was followed by days and days of rain—Recife rain. The air was humid with sticky heat.

His new life was very different from the life he had led in Paris. The house was melancholy; the rain did not let up, and his mother's unhappiness showed no sign of abating. Perhaps she would always be the same sorrowful widow who had met him all in black, with a long crepe veil and black gloves, wiping her eyes with a black handkerchief. She was as unhappy as though her son's presence consoled her very little, if at all, for the loss of her companion of nearly half a century. As an academic doctor with no clinical experience, Paulo understood this only in part; as a son, he felt frustrated by his failure to take his father's place in the affections of his widowed mother. His inability to do so piqued his vanity as a living son whose father, even after his death, held a more important place than he in his mother's heart.

For his own part, Paulo felt that he had been restored to a maternal Brazil that he had missed while living among Frenchmen who were fraternal at best and Frenchwomen who were not always fraternal. He had almost made up his mind to stay in Brazil, to keep his mother company, and to try to reintegrate himself into an environment that he felt in some ways truly his own. However, other facets of this tropical environment, with its excessive sunlight and color, made him feel as though he had returned from Europe a foreigner and could never be a native again unless he could somehow go back to his childhood and begin in contact with the Brazilian earth a new, instinctive life to be added to the intellectual experience he had gained in Europe, which he could certainly never forget. During long afternoons at home with his unhappy mother, who spent most of her time praying, he reflected on the problem of how his two lives, his two experiences, might be blended into one. Sometimes she wept as she prayed on her knees in the room where the statues of the saints were kept. Mother and son could always hear the singing of the birds the dead man had raised so tenderly, bringing the widow's loss poignantly home to her—a mission carried out rudely by the bellbird and sweetly by the canaries.

One of Paulo's few pleasures in that somber house— which was still furnished just as it had been in the days when his fond parents had spoiled their little boy and allowed him to play train with jacarandá chairs, which he and the pickaninny who lived in the house would push and pull into a row— was receiving the visits of his friends, who, after the news of his return had been published in the papers, began to call upon him, solemnly dressed in black to present their condolences. He conversed with these acquaintances—who sometimes hinted teasingly that his absence in Paris had doubtless been prolonged by the wiles of a certain Frenchwoman who had wound Paulo around her little finger—feeling, as he did so, a desire to re-adapt himself to his Brazilian environment, from which Europe had in fact alienated him (after all, seven years are seven years, not seven days!), and a necessity to relive his pre-intellectual past. Those persons who were still linked to that more intuitive period of his education could aid him, Paulo felt, in the adventure of reliving his own past and harmonizing it with his European experience.

Hence the eagerness with which Paulo sought out the family's old Negro servants, some of whom were former

slaves. The oldest of them, however, had died. The only
one left was Esperança, now a deaf, broken-down old
black woman whom he had known long ago by the lyrical
name bestowed on her capriciously by her master, a
baron with a university degree who liked to give his
slave-women names of that kind: Esperança, Felicidade,
Prazeres.[1]

Esperança had lived a life of ease in the Tavares
household. She belonged to her Massa and Missus, nobody else. Her life was that of a black relative of her
aristocratic white folk. The younger servants called her
Dona Esperança, for all the world as though she were the
prima donna of a Spanish theatrical troupe. But now,
deaf and decrepit as she was, she could be of little help to
Paulo in his attempt to relive his intimate, instinctive
past. There was nothing left but the memories conjured
up by her voice and manners, which were those of a pampered slave—her whole personality that of a woman at
death's door but still alive who, deaf and doddering as she
was, put him into direct contact with his long-dead childhood.

Another witness of that childhood was his family's
house, which was almost exactly as it had been in the old
days. It still held the same jacarandá furniture bedecked
with laces and ribbons, the same chandeliers, the same
statues of saints presiding over a sanctuary almost as
grand as a chapel. Still another reminder came from
those old friends of his boyhood, the trees in the garden;

[1] Hope, Happiness, Pleasure.

especially from a certain mango tree, stouter and more full of branches than the others, which he sometimes had climbed to daydream, as only children can dream, while perched on one of the highest boughs of the old tree, which was so hospitable to little boys tired of household routine and adult company.

On the day of his homecoming Paulo had inquired about the pickanniny, Gregório. Gregório? Had Paulo forgotten that Gregório had died years and years before? He remembered then that his father had written him about it. Gregório had died a horrible death: a capoeira [2] had knifed him in the stomach for no reason at all. Gregório, who had always doted on marching music, had died to the sound of a march. The bully had cut open his stomach, shouting "Viva Zemariano!" [3]

Another of Paulo's recollections was of one of his father's birds, a xexéu [4] who had been the apple of the old man's eye. The little creature had flown off one day, and the house had been thrown into an uproar. Old Tavares had been prostrated with a migraine. The neighbors had turned out *en masse* to search for the bird that had flown, as though it belonged to everyone in the neighborhood and not only to Tavares. The broken-hearted old man had put an ad in the newspapers, promising a reward to anyone who could bring the faithless little xexéu back to

[2] A practitioner of Afro-Brazilian leg-wrestling; a ruffian.
[3] The abolitionist José Mariano Carneiro da Cunha, mentioned in Chapter xii.
[4] A native Brazilian bird of the *icteridaceous* family.

147

him unharmed or wounded, scratched by the claws of a greedy cat or bruised by the slingslot of some boyish hunter.

It was no use; the xexéu had never been found. It was gone for good, and would never again he petted and pampered by its owner. What had happened to it? Had it fallen into the hands of another bird fancier? Or, awkward and half-crippled, like so many birds brought up in cages, had it been caught by the claws of some cat prowling in the neighborhood? They had never found out. Paulo remembered that his father had let the xexéu's cage remain empty for a long time, in the vague hope that the ungrateful little bird might return one day to his hospitable prison. It was an ingenuous hope on the part of old Tavares, who eventually replaced the xexéu with a cardinal.

15

FOR PAULO as a boy, the charm of his father's collection of birds lay not so much in the little creatures themselves as in the other bird fanciers who gathered on the veranda every Sunday to drink coffee, sip "white lightning" or cane liquor mixed with the juice of tamarinds or passion fruit, and eat cornmeal mush. Old Tavares treated some of these men as intimately as though they were people of his own class, which made Dona Teresa furious. "The idea of treating that riff-raff as though they were folks!" she would exclaim.

Tavares paid no attention to her. Paulo noticed that his father thought of people who raised birds as a class apart from the social considerations on which his mother, and particularly his aunt, put so much emphasis: "child" was one class to them, "nigger boy" another; "proper folks" were one thing, "white trash" another, and the two groups were never to be treated as equals. Tavares, on the other hand, did treat the bird fanciers, almost all of whom were "trash" and one of whom had the reputation of being a swindler in deals that had nothing to do with canary trading, as though they were his equals. He discussed the problems of bird raising with them with a total lack of ceremony. Dona Teresa was heard to remark more than once that it would not have surprised her to hear "those low, vulgar people" addressing her husband with the familiar "tu" and calling him by his nickname, Juca.

Paulo had become fond of one of the "low, vulgar people" who was not really "low" at all. He came from an aristocratic Serinhaém family and was, in fact, a distant relative of Dona Teresa. His speech was slow and drawling, as though he was sleepy and at the same time convinced of his superiority over his listeners. He appeared to be scornful of other people, as though anyone who wanted to hear him out would have to be patient: he was not going to talk any faster in order to make himself agreeable, much less subservient, to anyone. Life had diminished him in Dona Teresa's exacting eyes; in his own eyes, he was still the son of an aristocratic planter. The fact that he went without a necktie was of no importance; he was a gentleman.

He had never come into his paternal inheritance. "Rascality on the part of those barons against the widow of a man who was not a baron because he didn't want to be one" was his rather cryptic explanation; and Paulo liked to hear him talk about his life as a boy on the plantation. He had taken part in adventures that no one indulged in any more, such as perverse tricks, and worse, played on Negroes at a time when Negroes were plentiful. He had even helped smuggle contraband African slaves from boats onto the beaches of Serinhaém until the Emperor and the British discovered the forbidden trade, which had been an exciting adventure for some gentlemen in those days. The father of Chico Canary—or Chico the Birdman —had evidently been one of them. According to his son, he had been a brave man who feared neither the Emperor nor the English. After his father's death and the loss of the plantation, Chico Canary had become a bundle of rags and tatters. Not only had he been left penniless; he had no talent whatever for making a living.

He had gone to live in Recife with a Negro woman named Luzia, who sold fruit and vegetables and lived near the Church of São Gonçalo. Dona Teresa hated the thought that a blond, good-looking man like Chico, who was skinny but perfectly able to work, and the son of a plantation owner to boot, should live off the earnings of a Negro fruit- and vegetable-seller.

Chico's only occupation was raising birds, and he was a master of the art. He knew better than anyone else what each bird should be fed, and he was miraculously skillful at curing sick birds, his own and those of others. Even the most poverty-stricken, barefoot raiser of birds could count on Chico to cure his sick fledglings for nothing. People said that he had never lost a single one.

He kept his birds in cages that were so clean they glittered. Once Paulo had gone with his father to see Chico Canary's birds and had found there a man who immediately impressed the boy by his bearing, his figure, and his general air of a youthful grandee. Instead of shrinking before this majestic giant, Chico seemed to be vying with his visitor in polished manners and upright bearing. His skinny, rather stoop-shouldered figure had all at once stiffened into an almost military posture. Paulo missed not a single word the stranger spoke. He listened attentively, sure that the person to whom his father, more interested in Chico's birds than in the princely-looking man, had not introduced him, must be someone very important. When Paulo asked in a low voice who the man was, his father, as though suddenly remembering his manners, turned away from the birds and presented his son to the stranger: "Dr. Nabuco, this is my Paulo."

Joaquim Nabuco had smiled as he shook the little boy's hand. Paulo could still remember his grave words of praise, not so much for the birds as for the spotlessly clean cages: "You can tell that Chico had Dutch ancestors." From the darkness of the front room of the grocery store shone a wide, white smile that was almost laughter: Luzia's smile. Luzia, sitting among green cabbages, orange tangerines, yellow bananas, and fat red tomatoes, with a bright, multi-colored shawl around her strong, black shoulders, looked to Paulo like a Moorish enchantress from one of the stories about which he was beginning to be skeptical, but which he had not yet forgotten. If her skin had been only a few shades lighter, she could have passed for a princess wearing a turban instead of a golden crown.

Nabuco had said good-bye with vigorous handshakes all around, which make Tavares exclaim: "Bloody Englishman!"

Chico added the comment: "It's a shame the boy's turned into such a proper Englishman."

Chico had stood up straighter than Paulo had ever seen him, saying: "I still have enough Serinhaém Rocha Wanderly blood in me to talk to a Paes Barreto do Cabo [1] man to man." Paulo had also heard the canary fancier say: "A Wanderley's never spineless unless he wants to be!" And, speaking to Paulo: "Don't forget you have my people's blood in your veins, and that—Englishman's blood, too!" as he pointed to Nabuco as he strolled down the sidewalk, looking at São Gonçalo Church as if he had never seen it before. Paulo noticed that Luzia was still smiling a vast half-moon smile of contentment because Dr. Nabuco had shaken her hand too, and was repeating: "God bless that beautiful man Nhô Quim! [2] God bless him!" and Paulo had heard her speak this other phrase: "He's the best friend us folks has got! God bless him! God bless him!"

Paulo recalled that as soon as they had gone home again he had asked his mother to give him his colored pencils and drawing books. Still under the spell of what he had seen that day, he had drawn and colored a Nabuco whom he remembered as a handsome giant with black moustaches and, standing beside him, a Luzia who had the same strength and beauty. He had tried to draw

---

[1] Joaquim Nabuco was descended, on his mother's side, from the Paes Barretos, one of the oldest and most aristocratic families of Pernambuco.

[2] *Nhô* is another colloquial variant of *Senhor; Quim* a variation of *Quincas,* the diminutive form of Joaquim.

the Negress's smile: her beautiful white teeth shining against her purplish-black skin. He did not succeed; he knew that it was not in his power to capture a smile like Luzia's. He took special pains with her shawl, instead; and no longer bothering to be exact, he gave as many colors as he had colored pencils to the vegetable-seller's shawl and turban, which reminded him of the crown of a princess.

For a long time Paulo remembered those two outstandingly beautiful images: that of Joaquim Nabuco and that of Chico Canary's Luzia, as the grocery woman was known in some circles, while in others it was Chico who was sometimes called Luzia's Chico. It was rather a comical affair, which Paulo remembered hearing his family comment upon at the supper table. Paulo felt that the two images—Nabuco's and Luzia's—had cast a powerful spell over him. Later he realized that their fascination had stemmed from the fact that they had been the first two revelations of human beauty his childish eyes had ever seen: the man and the woman of extraordinary beauty; the handsome white man and the handsome Negress. He had always thought his mother was pretty, but now he realized that Luzia was prettier still: beautiful, he was to call her years later, when he had learned something about the relative meanings of words. Nor did his father, whom he had always thought of as the kind of man he wanted to be when he grew up, possesses the bearing, the height, the gaze, the handsome features, that had instantly caught his imagination in Joaquim

Nabuco. With these two examples of physical beauty—
Nabuco and Luzia—in his mind's eye, Paulo remembered
that he had begun to distinguish in human beings, not in
pictures but in the flesh, the beautiful from the merely
pretty.

The handsome Nabuco had asked him whether he
liked to catch birds, and in his confusion he had not
known whether to say yes or no. It was just as well, for
Nabuco had added: "I would rather watch the birds flying free," and had made a gesture that Paulo was to admire years afterward in Nabuco the orator as he spoke
about freedom, not for birds but for Negroes who were
still enslaved. The confused child could hardly say
"Thank you" to Luzia when she gave him some sweet-
smelling plums that she had picked out one by one for
Seu Tavares's little boy. Paulo knew only that he had felt
ennobled by the kindnesses shown him by that fine-looking white man and the beautiful Negress who had looked
to him, from his very first sight of her, like a Moorish
enchantress, a princess who would only have to be white
for her superiority to be revealed fully to all. But why
would she have to be white? Wasn't Our Lady of the
Rosary Our Lady, and wasn't she black?

Paulo remembered a frightening dream he had had
about Luzia when he had almost reached adolesence and
had already made his First Communion. He had never
been able to understand that dream. The Negress had
appeared in her radiant beauty, more beautiful than Our
Lady of the Rosary, but not smiling. The smile that had

lighted her face the day he had seen her with Nabuco had vanished. Her countenance was so grave—so stony, even —that the sight of her filled him with fear. She looked very beautiful, but it was a harsh beauty, lacking something that the boy, who was still a virgin, was used to seeing in the beauty of the women who were closest to his childhood: his mother, the aunt who was his godmother, and Esperança. Reaching for the boy with enormous hands out of proportion to her womanly figure, only slightly taller than that of other women, the dream Luzia seemed to turn into a monster: a kind of octopus-woman coming to snatch him from his mother's lap with those huge hands, as though he were a bird cowering in its nest.

Paulo had awakened with a lump in his throat, wanting to cry out and not even able to speak. He had calmed himself by praying and concentrating on the innocent blue of his dreams as a pious boy whom the priests encouraged to emulate St. Louis Gonzaga. Something told him that Luzia's memory caused him to sin against chastity. Luzia's angry look in his dream struck him as that of a woman who was surprised that Seu Tavares's little boy should be taking longer than other boys to become a man, to know a woman. From that time on, Luzia's image became for him that of a woman who, though even more beautiful than his mother, was also her enemy. Why, he did not know. Why should Luzia be his mother's antagonist in that dream which disturbed him so?

He had other dreams about the woman from Bahia. In one of them he saw her in a jungle, tearing mysterious red lianas from the trees and making a sauce with them, and then holding the gleaming scarlet sauce of lianas and walking toward Paulo with a menacing air. The handsome Luzia had become more threatening than seductive to the child; but even in the form of a terrible antimother, she was seductive nevertheless.

16

AFTER VISITING Recife's suburbs, Paulo went a little farther afield—to Olinda. It was in Olinda that he had left José Maria studying for the priesthood when he had sailed for Europe.

Dona Sinhá's son had remembered all his short life those first experiences as a seminary student in Olinda. He had recounted some of them to his friend Tavares and had also recorded them in his diary—a notebook full of phrases in Latin, which old Gaspar kindly permitted me to read. They were terrible experiences for the boy.

When José Maria woke on his second day in Olinda, far from his mother, the room was still dark. It seemed more like the end of night than the beginning of day. The boy opened his eyes wide in astonishment at not being at home with his mother. He found himself in the seminary at Olinda. A wild wind moaned in the coconut palms, and he heard the half-mournful, half-angry sound of waves breaking on the sand, waves not like those of São José do Ribamar.

It was not cold, but the boy felt an indefinable lack of warmth which made him shiver. He missed his mother dreadfully. She had always looked pretty to him, even when her hair was piled hastily on top of her head, the

way she wore it around the house early in the morning;
and she was always so gentle and sweet, especially at
night. It was she who put him to bed and heard him say
his prayers, put the aromatic powder on his toothbrush,
and even washed his feet after she or black Sinhama had
searched for chiggers, which every so often announced
their presence to the child, even before the tender search
of his mother or Sinhama, by an itching as familiar and
welcome to him as the pinprick of pain that he felt when
the insect, often replete with blood, was extracted with a
needle whose point had been sterilized in a flame and was
hot to the touch. It was his mother Sinhá who came to
wake him every morning bringing hot milk sprinkled
with a few drops of coffee, and sponge cake which she
had warmed so that it seemed freshly made in the oven
of some magic bakery for the fretful child, who had been
spoiled by the good cooking of Dona Sinhá and Sinhama,
each trying to outdo the other in creating mouth-watering
delicacies to arouse his languid appetite.

It was that feeling of warmth, milk, and mother which
José Maria missed and which made his first awakening in
Olinda like that of a child abandoned in the dark and the
cold. Orphans in asylums must have a similar awakening, he thought, but with one difference: orphans did not
know what a mother's tenderness was like.

José Maria felt as though he had been cast adrift in a
silence broken by nothing but the sound of the sea and
the sea wind. His ears missed the small, early morning
sounds he knew and loved, which made of São José do

Ribamar a world in which life began to stir as each new day—weekday or Sunday—brought to his ears its characteristic sounds, anticipating the sensations that the house, yard, and the street would later give him through his eyes and nose, and sometimes through his hands and bare feet. His feet were even more restless, more avid for exploration than his hands; but they were less capable of sinning.

In Olinda, José Maria's eyes could see nothing but darkness, which was not total darkness only because it was permeated with a pungent smell—an almost visible, tangible smell. The odor evidently came from the other boys who were there, like him, to outgrow their childhood and learn to be priests. Perhaps it was the smell of sex repressed, like José Maria's, for the sake of Jesus and Holy Mother Church; but José Maria did not know that. He could only feel the strong, thick, sticky smell come out of the dark and penetrate his being—the smell of sex repressed but not defeated.

How many of the boys in that room had, like José Maria, come straight from their homes and the scent of their mothers? How many of them were there in that big house? José Maria had only a vague idea of the history of the seminary. All he knew was that it had once been a Jesuit school with young boarders, many of whom later had become priests. They had left their mothers, their mothers' roots, their mothers' warmth, their mothers' scents, their grandmothers and sisters, to be left alone in the midst of other cold, sad, solitary children and priests, deprived of the comforting presence of all who were dear to them, except, of course, Our Lady and Jesus and the saints. And all of them gave off the same acrid odor, which seemed to fill the seminary with an air alien to that of their homes.

It was the only way they could become priests, José Maria knew; but it was a pity, thought the boy, still full of the warmth and the scent of his mother. He was still so close to her that he had not even learned to pray by himself.

How much better it would be if he, José Maria, could learn to be a priest and still belong to his mother, and smell like his mother and not like a priest—not like a monk—not even like Dom Vital.

Now he could visualize his mother waking up in the house in São José do Ribamar to the sound of Sinhama's voice: "Sinhá! Sinhá! Wake up, Sinhá!" She always awakened in a twinkling, so light was her sleep.

She liked to heat her son's milk and spone cake herself: for "meu fiinho," as she used to say, in her Portuguese in which the sound of *lh* was missing. Perhaps at this moment she was singing, as she sometimes did early in the morning, old songs that always seemed to speak of May, the month of Mary. Perhaps she was opening the street door and saying good morning to Dona Eulália, another of the Square's early risers. They would wait at the door together for the man who sold cuscuz.[1] Sinha would call to Inácia or Benedita inside the house that

[1] Steamed cornmeal or rice mixed with coconut.

lunch would be chicken and rice, but good yellow rice, "the kind José Maria likes." And they should be sure to keep an eye out for the mangaba [2] woman and buy some "for José Maria." There were probably still a few mangabas—the last of the season—around Prazeres.

José Maria remembered that he had awakened in his bed in São José do Ribamar with the feeling that the house was already echoing with his name. For his widowed mother and the black servants, it was always José and Maria; boy and girl, child and youth on the threshhold of manhood, already taking the place of men who had once been loved in the flesh and now were loved only in spirit, by a Sinhá whose husband had not been the ideal spouse she had dreamed of. She often admitted as much to her son, confessing her thoughts to him as though he were already full grown and a priest. Her ideal had been her father, old Albuquerque Wanderley (more Wanderley than Albuquerque), who had brought her up as lovingly as his wife could have—Sinhá's mother, Dona Rita, who had died young and had hardly known her daughter. Sinhá had grown up among so many pictures of her dead mother in the flower of her youth that she sometimes felt as though she could remember her, or as though Dona Rita was still living among her daughter, son, and husband. The widower kept a trunk full of clothes that Sinhá's mother had worn, and on his more sentimental days he would open the trunk and encourage Sinhá and the servant women to handle his dead wife's

[2] Wild fruit, a variety of dogbane.

dresses, even the bridal gown, which he had put away with so much love. José Maria grew up surrounded by memories of his grandmother, who was still an almost tangible presence in the house, and looked after by a grandfather who was more like a father to him than his own father, who had died of the fever when he was only thirty years old and had been, even when alive, less a man than a shadow of one in a house which his death left hardly more empty than it had been before. It was almost as though Sinhá had never had a husband or José Maria a father in any real sense of the word.

José Maria was the darling of his mother and grandfather from the day he was born. They monopolized him to such an extent that his father seemed left out, useless, and slightly ridiculous in the house in Ribamar, the only Republican among devotees, not only of Our Lady but of Princess Isabel. José Maria was more of a girl-child than a boy in the jealous eyes of his mother and grandfather, who were eager to watch the unfolding of a life that was almost a resurrection of their Rita, the dead woman so lovingly remembered in her former home that it was as though she were being gradually reborn in a José Maria who, through a mistake on the part of someone—the silly father, most likely—had been born a boy. His grandfather had expected and hoped for a girl, who would have been named Maria Rita, after the dead woman whose dresses, trimmed with yards of yellowed lace, were folded away in the trunk, whose faded pictures were kept in an album with a mother-of-pearl cover, and whose jewels were encased in a silver box lined in a blue so faded that it seemed to José Maria a sad caricature of the blue he loved—the blue of the ocean, that looked bluer to him than the sky of Recife itself, which was rarely cloudless. José Maria sensed, with an intuition, that he was petted and loved because he seemed to bring his dead grandmother to life again for his grandfather, and even for his mother. He could hardly have felt otherwise, after hearing so often that he had his grandmother's eyes, his grandmother's smile, and even his grandmother's walk—a grandmother who seemed to dissolve into the image of Dona Sinhá.

Now, as he woke up alone in a big, strange house in which there were no portraits of Dona Rita among the pictures of the saints, what seemed strangest to him was the knowledge that in that house he was nothing but an insignificant new pupil, with no mother to take care of him and feed him his milk sprinkled with coffee and his hot sponge cake soaked in milk and crumbled into mush.

He took courage from the example of Dom Vital, of whom Dona Sinhá had often spoken and whom Pius IX had once called his "caro Olinda." Dom Vital had no doubt suffered as José was suffering now. He too had been torn by Holy Mother Church from the loving arms of his gentle mother and the succulent tidbits prepared by his black mammy. The Olinda seminary was a bridge from one mother to the other, a bridge that he would have to cross, suffering and rejoicing in his suffering.

17

ONE of the images of Brazil which had remained in Paulo's mind through all the years of his stay in France was of a country that had not only a great deal of land but also a great deal of water. One day he astonished a Frenchman on whom the drought of 1877 in Ceará had made such a strong impression that he thought of Brazil as a fearfully arid, tropical country by telling him: "My province alone, Pernambuco, has more water than all of France put together."

He remembered the coastal waters, the plantation rivers, the waterfalls in the forests. He had never seen the Paulo Afonso Falls, but the memory of swims below the rapids and the adventures of his Madalena boyhood in the rip-tide waters of the Capibaribe River was sufficient to make him remember Brazil as a country that was hot, certainly, but was also refreshed by an abundance of water.

Of the Carnivals he had celebrated in his boyhood and adolesence in Recife, his most pungent memory was that of a festival that was decidely pagan and was also, in a way, a glorification of water. The St. John's Day festivals in June were a celebration of fire; the Brazilian Carnival was a celebration of water. In those days the inhabitants of Recife amused themselves during Carnival by throwing water on one another. The more fastidious were satisfied with refreshing limes scooped out and filled with water, while the others gave themselves over to veritable street battles, violently splashing one another with water that was not always of the cleanest.

It is understandable, then, that Paulo should have felt pleasure at seeing again in Recife a festival as liquidly Brazilian as Carnival.

Carnival was not, of course, a festival in which Paulo, still in deep mourning, could participate. He could not try to relieve the frolics so intimately linked to his first youthful adventures—not only the harmless hugging and petting with girls from good families, who were sometimes at least partially successful in evading the vigilance of their parents during those celebrated three days, but also the more daring adventures with mulatto women of the kind that made a special point of seducing white youths with their bacchanalian enticements and initiating them into the crudest sort of physical love-making. Paulo's first complete experience with a woman had occurred during Carnival, when he had been dragged by one of those mulatto girls to the foot of a flight of steps in the Rua Larga do Rosário.

Paulo did not, however, remain entirely aloof from Carnival. One day he was invited to partake of fritters at the home of Fonseca, his father's old business partner and one of the most prominent members of a Carnival club called Cavalheiros da Época.[1] Some of his adolescent experiences came back to him as he crossed the streets, cheered by the smiles of gently bred white girls and the scandalous laughter of mulatas who looked exactly like those he remembered from his youth.

Fonseca told him of the triumphs that the Cavalheiros da Época had had in the past few years. Paulo should not think it was merely a social club; it was also civic-minded. The club made use of Carnival to educate the people; it practiced the best kind of citizenship, as, indeed, it had ever since Abolition. The Cavalheiros had done their part to make sure that the Carnival of 1889 would be a veritable paean to abolitionism. The Carnival of '88 had amounted to a revolution: it had made terrible accusations against the barons, the slave-owning aristo-crats, and the government of Pedro Banana.[2]

Paulo knew that although Fonseca was a great friend of the sugar planters, whose interests he defended in the Market together with Tavares, who had many rural rela-tives, he had nevertheless been an abolitionist and a partisan of free labor. He had even accepted the idea of Chinese immigration as a solution, provided that the Chinese were free men and not coolies. He had argued with Tavares about the subject. Apropos of those argu-ments, he remarked to Paulo: "You know how your father was: indifferent about a lot of things. I believe he actually thought that it would have been best for Brazil to

[1] Gentlemen of the Age.
[2] Pedro the Milksop, a contemptuous term for Dom Pedro II.

go on being a slave-holding Empire. Not that he was one of those cranky conservatives. Not a bit of it. He even knew parts of some of Nabuco's speeches by heart. Don't you remember, Paulo?"

Old Tavares could not abide to hear anyone speak ill of "handsome Quincas" [3] or say that "Quincas the Handsome" was a seditious firebrand. The abolitionist cause did not, however, arouse his enthusiasm. He distrusted the Republic and some of its propagandizers. He even distrusted abolitionists if their ideas were different from those of Quincas. He would have been content for Brazil to remain a monarchy forever.

"And what about the abolitionist Carnival of '89?" Paulo inquired of Fonseca in a half-mocking tone that the sugar king did not seem to notice. Paulo saw that Fonseca was only very slowly becoming aware of the fact that Tavares's son had come back from Europe not entirely convinced that the Abolition of '88 and the Republic of '89 had been advantageous to Brazil. He had already told Fonseca that the fifteenth of November [4] was not much spoken of in France, *except to lament the rudeness with which the Republicans had treated the old Emperor, who was better known in that country than was Brazil itself. As for the abolition of slavery, no one but a small group of French radicals had even taken notice of the event.* Paulo himself shared the ideas of his discreet and cautious father, who had been in favor of a

[3] Joaquim Nabuco.
[4] The proclamation of the Republic in 1889.

gradual liberation of the slaves under the Empire, in thinking that Nabuco had been too precipitate. Not agriculture alone, but the whole country, was suffering the ill effects of the so-called Golden Law.[5]

At the moment, however, Paulo was interested less in the disappointment that his ideas might be causing his father's friends than in hearing Fonseca describe this civic carnival of his, which he considered the most important—as a civic carnival, he emphasized, pronouncing the word "ci-vic" with didactic emphasis—that Recife had ever beheld. It was obvious that Fonseca had contributed money as well as ideas to this prime example of a civic carnival. The real organizer of the pageant displayed by the Cavalheiros da Época had been, as Fonseca explained to Paulo, a well-educated man, a university graduate, who was also something of a Bohemian. No one could ever be sure when he was taking himself seriously and when he was not. This time, though, Fonseca declared, the young man whose name he could not recall— "a beer-crazy poet!"—had taken the thing seriously. The result had been a splendid pageant that had dazzled the city of Recife. True, there were amusing touches here and there: after all, it was Carnival. But it had been, in the main, a lesson in citizenship. And citizenship was what the country needed. After expressing these opinions with a pedagogical air—opinions that were, to Paulo's way of thinking, too grave to be mixed up with Carnival —Fonseca asked Dona Quininha to offer their guest an-

[5] The law of 1888 emancipating the slaves.

other helping of fritters. Although Paulo could not enjoy Carnival this year, let him at least have his fill of fritters. Carnival without fritters wasn't Carnival; but then, fritters without Carnival were not as tasty. One had to enjoy the three days of Carnival in order to appreciate such delicacies, which tasted good only at the proper time of year. No one made fritters as well as Quininha.

"Oh, no!" that lady protested. "Don't you remember the fritters Dona Sinhá used to make?" Paulo remained silent in tactful neutrality as he tasted the savory fritters offered to him for the second time, which were undeniably delicious. But if his memory did not deceive him, they were not quite so light, did not melt in the mouth quite so readily, as Dona Sinhá's. This reminded him not only of Dona Sinhá but also of José Maria. He remembered that it has been at Carnival time that the aggressively male boys had taken most delight in harassing José Maria by calling him Missy. Some of them would always shout into the poor thing's ear: "Why don't you put on a woman's dress, Missy?"

Fonseca, cheerfully crunching a fat fritter, brought some clippings from a desk drawer: he wanted to show Paulo his club's pageant in the Carnival of '89, and the news of the great triumph the Cavalheiros da Época had scored with their seven floats. Everyone knew that the members of his club were solid citizens. Some of the most prominent businessmen, and even rich sugar merchants, had made large contributions. They were not the only ones, either: some of the members were sugar planters who spent Carnival in Recife, where they stayed at the homes of buyers who lodged them as though they were relatives. For Paulo's information, however, notwithstanding all the conservative elements who made contributions to the club, one of its pageants, the 1889 one, had had rather a republican, as well as an abolitionist, theme. Paulo should keep in mind the fact that since 1888 a large part of the conservative class had come around to the republican way of thinking, and that this was evident in the Carnival of '88 and still more in that of '89.

The newspaper clipping contained a description of the pageant of the Cavalheiros da Época in 1889. First of all, of course, *came the float with the club banner—a splendid banner, borne by three Cavalheiros in claw-hammer coats and gloves, who looked like ministers of state.* Fonseca calculated the cost in several contos de reis.[6] It was a fine piece of work. Embroidered on it were the words "XPTO Londó."

Then came an *"apotheosis of abolitionism."* Paulo could read for himself: *Two slave-owning planters with two victims of their ignoble commerce.* The name on that float was *Oppression of the Captives*—very pretty. There were people in the crowd who wept as it went along the Rua Nova. Dona Quininha had even heard of fainting fits.

The third float was entitled: *The Law of May 13th Has Made Us Equal.* The article explained: *A typical group of two land-owners and two freemen forget sordid social*

[6] A conto is worth 1,000 mil-reis (now called cruzeiros).

prejudices in the ease of social companionship! The
fourth was *the future representatives of Brazil—two
richly dressed Negroes, whose pretentious physiognomies
show an evident aptitude for great reforms.* Here it
seemed plain to Paulo that the intention of whoever had
organized the pageant was to make fun of abolitionism as
it had been carried out in Brazil. The sly intentions of the
"beer-crazy poet" were even more obvious in the seventh
and last float, coming after the fifth, in which *"two emi-
nent politicians" regarded the future of the National Empire through binoculars,* and the sixth, *an allegory representing the Republic.* The seventh and last was ironically
entitled *Equality, Liberty, Fraternity . . . of Conveni-
ence!!!* and was described in the newspaper thus: *"A
group of three republican mestizos—including a university graduate, a fifth-year law student, and a government
employee!!!"*

The description of this pageant interested Paulo even
more than Fonseca had supposed that it would. He had
returned from France with ideas which, as Fonseca had
already begun to realize, were not the ideas commonly
associated in Brazil with the French. Sympathizing very
little with the simple-minded egalitarian republicanism
that had taken the place of abolitionism almost over-
night, he found all of these innovations superficial at
best; and it seemed to him significant that in important
Brazilian cities like Recife, where what Fonseca called
"civic carnivals" took place, persons of wit should take
advantage of the opportunity to express their criticism of

abolitionism and republicanism while those of good faith, provided with funds by the so-called conservative classes, paid homage to these innovations by means of allegorical —or rhetorical—floats, to an extent that surprised Paulo.

He recalled having read the following sentence in a Brazilian newspaper which his father had sent to him in France at the time of the proclamation of the Republic in 1889: *"Brazil has resolved its problem peacefully and naturally, as a wise man solves an astronomical or mathematical problem in the peace of his study."* Paulo now saw that that had not been exactly the case: *there had also been civic carnivals, in which homage had been paid to the triumphant Republic, since the beginning of 1888. Ever since the Carnival of '88.*

Fonseca interrupted Paulo's meditations by serving him a glass of port and lowering his voice, evidently to make some political confidence. "You know very well, Paulo, that I always had republican leanings. I was always one of the imbaronáveis. . . ." [7]

"One of the what?" asked the half-French Brazilian. Fonseca repeated the neologism, stressing it as he had stressed the adjective "civic," linked oddly to the substantive noun "carnival": im-ba-ro-ná-veis.

"Your father couldn't help agreeing with me," Fonseca went on. "The only thing was, your father got carried away by Nabuco and his notion of saving Brazil through federation and still keeping the monarchy. A poet's idea. I

---

[7] Literally, one who refused to defend the barons or to be made a baron by the Emperor.

think it was Martins—Martins Júnior, you know, a first-rate talent, even if he still doesn't know his way around in practical politics; a man just about your age, and he wears a pince-nez like yours—who wrote an article in *O Norte* saying exactly that: that Nabuco's idea was a poet's fantasy. Federation, reorganization, reform, could only come about in a republic. And it would take a republic to give commerce, industry, and agriculture the attention they deserved. The idea of federation under the monarchy had been, if I recall his words correctly, *a trace of superstition nesting in the brain of a great thinker.* He was referring to Nabuco, of course, and showing that he was even more of a poet than he was a thinker."

Fonseca got up again. He might still have that article from *O Norte.* He went to search for it in his desk, but immediately found instead, in a drawer that Paulo saw must be his ci-vic drawer, some other newspaper clippings that made him forget the one he had been looking for. Sitting down again in his rocking chair next to Paulo's, he began reading one of the articles in a loud, emphatic voice. It had been published in *O Norte* on November 23, 1889. "Listen to this, Paulo, just listen to this!" With oratorical flourishes, as though making a speech, Paulo read what he thought was the most important part of the article: ". . . *Europe, too, bows in reverence to this white caboclo of the American pampas and the dark mountain ranges of the Brazilian motherland, and, struck with awe as though by some political cataclysm, kisses his powerful hand and cries 'Hail!'* "

Fonseca then took up another clipping, this one from *A Era Nova* of December 15, 1889, more specific and more conservative in tone: "*Pernambuco business interests always received unfair treatment at the hands of the monarchical government. This explains the events which took place in the Paranaguá Ministry, which must still be fresh in the minds of those who were affected by them. Under the moderate regime we have adopted, if our politicians realize that commerce and agriculture are the two main sources of wealth in this country, they can, by passing wise laws, stimulate its inhabitants to engage in purposeful activity.*" *The writer then invoked the example of the great North American nation, especially Chicago,* "*where the pork-processing industry is acquiring astounding proportions.*" In view of all this, the journal advised, "*the commerce and agriculture of Pernambuco have a magnificient opportunity to choose men from among their ranks to represent them nationally, to make known their real necessities, and to demand co-operation for their progressive development.*" And Paulo should listen to this one last quotation: "*Business, absorbed in its own transactions, had no part whatever in political movements in the days of the Empire, feeling only the unhappy consequences of the errors of the latter, which, all of its old vitality gone, was fast approaching bankruptcy.*" It was sad to see "*the disconsolate appearance that not even the most prosperous firms could conceal . . . the gradual diminution that hard times had forced the merchants to carry out among their work force,*" who "*also began to fear that their hour of doom had struck."*

Paulo listened patiently to the rhetoric of his father's partner, who had become such an ardent Republican and abolitionist. It seemed to Paulo that as a sugar-trade aristocrat, the old man had come to think of himself since the advent of the Republic as a prince of commerce rather than a sugar planter. The young man could hardly fail to perceive in the "imbaronável," as Fonseca called himself, a desire to become a political leader of the Republic, after the manner of a doge of Venice rather than an imperial baron—as the representative of a force, that of business, which he felt strongly had been, like agriculture, scorned and neglected by the Empire.

Their ears were assaulted by the Carnival hubbub in the streets—the throwing of limes filled with water (which were becoming passé), tubes filled with water or paint (which were just coming into vogue), and confetti, was reaching its liveliest peak. Colored people, as happy as could be, were jumping, hopping, dancing, and singing with what remained of their old African exuberance. It was as though the emancipation proclamation of May 13th had made Carnival, for some of the freemen, more delightful than ever, a mingling of liberty and libertinage.

It was also true, however, that prominent men, white men, abolitionists, Republicans, and even some of the freemen, did not seem fired enough by enthusiasm to link civic fervor to the Carnival festivities as they had done in '88 and '89. Now they seemed dominated by a spirit of political criticism. Floriano [8] and Barbosa Lima [9] were increasing in stature, one in all of Brazil and the other in Pernambuco, and casting a rather sinister shadow over such enthusiasm. During Carnival it was becoming apparent, mused Paulo as he walked prudently home through the confusion of the festive streets before it grew dark, that Brazilians were no longer dazzled by Abolition and the Republic. The citizens of Pernambuco (to take his father's partner as an example) struck him as having lost their bearings; the "conservative classes" seemed a little hesitant to see the cause of Order embodied in a mysterious figure like Floriano. Paulo had noticed that even Fonseca, for all the eloquence with which he had read those journalistic effusions from the first lyrical, idyllic days of the Republic, did not seem entirely enthusiastic about the new statesman. However, as it was plain to Paulo that the new Republican was flirting with a possible political office, it was natural that he should assume the fervor of an adept of the institutions that had come to

[8] Marshall Floriano Peixoto (1839–95), hero of the war with Paraguay, was first Vice-President and, after the resignation of Marshall Deodoro da Fonseca, second President of the Brazilian Republic. During his term as President, the "Iron Marshall" severely crushed an armed revolt aimed at restoring the monarchy.

[9] Alexandre José Barbosa Lima (1862–1931) was a typical exponent of the republican generation of radical Contean Positivists. His political career as a federal deputy and senator extended, with few interruptions, from 1891 to 1930. He served as governor of Pernambuco from 1892 to 1896.

modernize the country—as he had repeated over and over to the young man, whose unprogressive ideas had bewildered him as a man educated in France. To Fonseca's way of thinking, the new institutions must not fail to attribute a greater importance to business. He thought that this point was of key importance.

18

PAULO was pleased when an old acquaintance who had been his companion in Amaro's Latin school and was now, like him, a doctor of medicine, came one morning with a horse and buggy to take him to visit the suburbs. They went to Ponte d'Uchoa, Poço da Panela, Apipucos— districts that were lapped by the most authentic waters of Recife.

Both young men set out wearing black suits, of course, and top hats, as befitted the sacerdotal profession of medicine. But inside those frock coats, thought Paulo with a smile, were two boys longing to free themselves from adult garb and prejudices by recapturing some of their childhood memories.

One of Paulo's happiest memories of Pernambuco was of swims he had enjoyed in its rivers. He was obsessed by the thought that in order to feel like a Brazilian once more, after so many years away from the country, he must go down to the river waters and immerse himself in them voluptuously, religiously, mystically, like the Hindus. It was as though he belonged even more to those waters than to the earth of Recife and the black clay of the plantation of his Pernambuco grandparents: earth and clay that he had trod in his childhood with the free,

brave, adventurous, questing, experimental, exploring
feet of a boy of the tropics, unhampered by shoes or slippers or clogs or galoshes or hunting boots; feet that ran
the risk of stepping on snakes and scorpions or being
stung by nettles. Naked feet that felt the texture, the dry
heat, the clinging cold, the fat, soft warmth that was almost like human skin, of the different kinds of tropical
earth. Feet that were pierced by chiggers in the loose sand
shaded by cashew and mango trees, and besmeared by
chicken dung in the kitchen gardens. Feet that sought
refreshing coolness in the water of irrigation ditches,
rainpools, or river shallows. Feet that became aristocratic
again only at night, when the chambermaid, as though
following a ritual, came to prepare them for sleep in a
bed lined with linen, picking out thorns, chiggers, and
the treacherous spikes of black nightshade, and bandag-
ing the cuts from broken glass and the chilblains caused
by unclean, stagnant water or humid earth, bathing and
cleaning them in preparation for sleep (the sleep of a
virgin at first, and later that of a semi-virgin) among the
purest, whitest, snowiest of sheets. Paulo came to believe
that for Brazilian boys who were brought up practically
barefoot, as he had been, those naked feet—so light and
free, so adventurous in the daytime, but tended by the
servant at night as though they were the feet of a fastidious girl—were an anticipation of sex in their experiences
with voluptuous contact. For his own part, he remembered as being related to, or precursors of, sexual pleasures which he had experienced later on, certain itchings

in his toes which followed the skillful, delicate extraction of stubborn chiggers by his mulatto nursemaid Rosa, a real artist at performing this minor surgery. Those pleasures had prepared him for sex, as though he and other boys like him had sex in the tips of their toes before it became concentrated in their sexual parts.

Paulo noticed, now that he had returned to Brazil after so many years of wearing shoes day in and day out in Europe, that his toes and the soles of his feet seemed to have preserved sensual impressions of the various earths of his country which enabled his memory to distinguish a variety of sensations connected with a variety of experiences. The sand on the beach in Olinda, for example, felt different from the sand at Brum, from that of the deep water where the Bath House was being constructed, and from that of Tamandaré, where he had been taken to spend a few months as a child by relatives who owned a plantation not far from the beach. At Tamandaré he had heard talk of an old female relation, described as a half-mannish, half-demonic figure of a woman, whom the inhabitants of the place had come to fear as they would have feared an apparition from another world. It seemed to Paulo that his feet had kept a particularly humid, voluptuous memory of the sands at Tamandaré, even the drier ones. Even when they ran in fear, spurred on by the cries of his little black comrades—"Here comes Dona Francisca!" "Here comes the old lady with the beard!" "Here comes the baroness with a switch in her hand!"— his feet could feel the caress of that sand, which was sometimes warm and sometimes humid. In Olinda it was just the opposite: the sand there was almost always warm, and sometimes hot, which also felt good to a child's feet.

How would that same sand, and the sand near the Bath House, feel now to his adult feet—his Europeanized Brazilian feet? They were feet that also remembered the delightful stickiness of mud on a rainy day, the kind that Esperança used to say would give him chilblains. He remembered the sand underneath the cashew trees, which Esperança used to say had more chiggers than sand, and the contact with the sidewalks and the paving stones of streets like those of São José; contacts that were more or less forbidden to Paulo. The streets were no place for a white boy to set his foot, but only for little Negroes who didn't mind stepping in horse and ox dung. His feet remembered what it had felt like to step in animal excrement in the cane fields, in fresh cow dung, and in chicken droppings that were still warm. Once he had walked into the house stinking of chicken dung, with one foot all smeared with it, and the aunt who was his godmother had made him take a bath and scrub himself with soap: he had done a disgraceful thing, and he must never do it again. His godmother was more fastidious and demanding, in many ways, than his mother. His mother would go into the hen house and feel the hens' posteriors with a pleasure that was incomprehensible to the other woman. He, Paulo, had been taught by his mother how to feel a hen and had become quite expert at it; he thought

it had given his forefinger a special sensitivity which
would be useful to him as a doctor. If his godmother had
had her way, little Paulo would never have set foot outside the house without boots on, for fear of snakes. Dona
Augusta's terror of snakes was almost a mania, and she
felt an equally strong repugnance for the animal excrement that stuck to her godson's feet as if they had been
the feet of a pickaninny. Dona Augusta, Paulo's godmother, drew a very firm line between little white boys
and pickaninnies, and between boys from good families
and boys who ran about in the streets.

All of these memories, and others which had lain dor-
mant in Paulo's memory, now rose to the surface. The
first thing he wanted to do was go to Brum and be reminded of his first swims in the ocean, when he had
stuck close to his father and clung to his mother's reas-
suring thick blue flannel bathing garments. Then, when
he was eight years old, he had begun to swim at Brum
with a professional lifeguard, going out into deeper and
deeper water and waving back at his mother. He would
have to pay a visit to Lacerda and "Daddy," the two most
famous swimming instructors of the childhood days
when he had first ventured to swim away from his
mother. They had been his first heroes—men who
seemed able to make the sea obey them, and who were
respected by the very waves. Lacerda seemed even more
a lord of the occasionally rough seas of Brum than
"Daddy." One of Paulo's dreams, when he had been eight
years old, had been to let the hot sun bronze him as it had

bronzed the lifeguards. Alas, the midday sun was almost always forbidden to him: the grownups said it would addle his brain. It had seemed odd to Paulo that it had not addled Daddy's brain—he had a lot of sense. It hadn't seemed to hurt Lacerda, either. Once Lacerda had explained to Paulo that it wasn't the midday sun that was bad for people's heads, but the full moon. He had never forgotten those words.

Paulo paid a visit to the Bath House, out on the reefs. It had still been unfinished when he had left for Europe. From the cutter taking him out to the ship, Paulo had gazed in nostalgic farewell at the Bath House, which was still under construction but was already familiar to him. That wood-and-iron pavilion built on the bare rock dividing the city from the sea had held a special fascination for him in his tropical Brazilian adolescence. It was said to be unique, unrivaled in any part of the world.

Now, returning again to his native Recife and seeing the finished Bath House in all its glory, Paulo was proud of that original Brazilian invention. It was truly a Recife originality, a Brazilian originality. Why did Brazil not have more native originalities like that Bath House?

Paulo found it full of Englishmen. He would have liked to remain there for several days, going barefoot and yet surrounded by the appurtenances of civilized living in the company of those Englishmen. He and his friend arranged to spend the rest of the afternoon at the Bath House, which was also known as the Medeiros House. They would dine there; the boat could wait.

Paulo shed his topcoat, took off his shoes and socks, and went down to the water's edge. He splashed in the foot bath, exclaiming repeatedly: "There's nothing like this in Europe, boy!" with a voluptuous pleasure which his friend thought rather exaggerated. Observing the joviality of the Englishmen, he remarked: "Just think what a good time those Englishmen must be having!" He went into a dressing room, put on his bathing suit, and dived into the salt water heart and soul.

With his whole body immersed in that gentle, warm ocean water, Paulo felt as though he had been restored to the source, the root, of all that was deepest in him. To Paulo, those waters were maternal.

The Bath House offered an ideal combination for the tropical European Paulo had become. While in free contact with water, sand, and reefs in a tropical temperature, he had within his reach English magazines and books in French in the reading room, English beefsteaks, and dressing rooms of French, if not English, comfort. It was not hot at all; a continuous gentle breeze blew from the east. The Bath House overlooked the winds and water. It was washed by the tides going in and out and caressed by every wind that blew, though the east wind fanned it most often. For Paulo, it was a glimpse of paradise. He would have liked to send his mother a message and spend the night there; but he saw that his friend was becoming slightly bored, and he did not want to leave his company.

After dinner they went back together "to Recife." It

seemed to Paulo that the waters were parting to let the prodigal son's boat pass through. How wonderful that Recife should have such a Bath House!

If Paulo's feet, and even his sex, seemed to have found a small lost paradise in the old Brazilian province of his childhood—his brown, humid, tropical boyhood—which had come back to him through contacts which were not merely sensual and intuitive but reached still more delicate zones of sensitivity, be nevertheless realized, when analyzing himself, that with every passing day his intelligence missed more keenly the intellectual atmosphere of Europe. He waited for the packet boat from Europe with impatient eagerness for letters, and above all for the magazine that was becoming more and more a part of him, the *Revue des Deux Mondes*. The *Revue* had become essential to his life as a doctor who had no necessity to practice. He was particularly attracted by its articles on frontiers of medicine as related to other sciences, as well as to art, literature, philosophy, and even religion. The *Revue des Deux Mondes*, in fact, brought Europe to the tropics.

It had long been a tradition in Paulo's family, as in other Brazilian families, to read—or at least to subscribe to, glance through, and put away on a bookshelf next to the classic works by Herculano and Castilho and the *Almanac of Luso-Brazilian Souvenirs*—the quintessentially European and yet more than European *Revue des Deux Mondes*. The family had begun subscribing to the magazine in his grandfather's time. The worthy planter had been tutored by a certain very learned chaplain, one of those priests who might weaken in their vows of chastity, but never in their loyalty to correct grammar and to Latin literature. Paulo remembered having witnessed the arrival, at his grandfather's plantation house in Serinhaém, of a red-bearded French engineer who had come in from the backlands, dust-covered and splashed with mud. After a bath that the Frenchman had taken in the Brazilian manner in his room, with the aid of a wooden tub and calabash gourd, with slaves bringing him kettles of hot water and leather bottles of old aguardente to "purify" the water, he had gone into the front room and, after browsing through the books in the big jacarandá bookcase, had almost jumped out of his skin with excitement at catching sight of the latest issue of the *Revue des Deux Mondes*. At last Paulo understood the French engineer's jubilation, which had seemed exaggerated to his childish eyes at the time. Now it was Paulo who all but danced with joy when the mail from Europe brought him a new issue of the *Revue*.

He thought of it as one of his French schoolmistresses. Paulo made a point of stressing the feminine gender of this intellectual influence, for he had learned from female as well as male teachers in France the art of discriminating, criticizing, and relishing literary and philosophical subtleties, which he had come to think of as essential but which could be appreciated only by men who, like Renan, had acquired a few feminine traits. In Paris he never failed to read old Buloz's review, certain that each new issue would reveal to him some new aspect of European culture filtered through the French mind, which was, to the half-French Brazilian, more critical, synthetical, and didactical than any other. Paulo recalled that Buloz's *Revue* had published articles by Stendhal, Thierry, Michelet; then Taine, Renan, Feuillet, and finally Chevreul, Berthelot, and Laugel, who had pointed out more clearly than anyone else, in Paulo's opinion, the importance of Pasteur's work, not only to medical science but also in the shaping of a whole new concept of human society. He could not forget that it was in the *Revue* that his attention had first been drawn to Marey's so-called graphic method. And then there was Quatrefages; he had read essays by that author in the *Revue*. It was in the pages of the *Revue* that he had first become aware, as a student of the humanities, of Darwin's theories of evolution, thanks to Quatrefages's articles. Once he had begun his medical studies in earnest, some of his time had been profitably spent in reading the *Revue's* excellent articles of interest to doctors, on serotherapy, vaccines, anaphylaxis—a whole cluster of facts and techniques made possible, even necessary, by the "new French revolution," as Paulo called the innovations brought about by Pasteur. It still seemed to Paulo that this revolution was diminishing the scope of the practicing physician in favor of the aggrandizement of medical science as a whole, and integrating that science into a general renovation of human knowledge.

"Still seemed," because Paulo felt a diminution of the

scientific spirit that had absorbed his adolescent mind. That spirit had begun to be supplanted in recent years by another way of looking at life, man, and the proper place of science in the knowledge of mankind. It was possible that this change in him was partly owing to a conversation he had had for two hours or more, on the train from Belgium to Paris, with a French Dominican priest. The Dominican had smilingly told him of a Church that by no means felt that it had been vanquished by the new science. And then he had spoken of science, with a knowledge of recent discoveries that was really astonishing. At the same time he had recommended new books by authors who were reacting against scientific materialism and finding in the Catholic Church, not a refuge for their disappointment, but a fulcrum that was historical and at the same time above history—an attitude impossible to science, which was subhistorical by nature, added the priest, in words that Paulo had never forgotten—and which led to a vigorous concept of life, of mankind, and of knowledge, in which science was not a goddess but a servant. A useful, valuable, obliging servant; but nothing more.

Thanks to this unforgettable traveling companion, to whom Paulo had propounded all of his Positivist and Spencerian arguments in vain, the Brazilian had acquired, on his return to Paris, every book by an Englishman named Newman that he could lay his hands on. Here was an Englishman who, when the scientific spirit was at its height in England, had turned his back on the new gods

—in the emphatic words of the Dominican—in order to enter the Catholic Church, a man with a lucid, critical, discerning intelligence which (the priest had remarked in an aside) was more French than English. It would be hard to find anyone as modern as this Newman. Paulo should read his books without delay.

Paulo read the books of the great English convert in French. Such was his enthusiasm for Newman that he set out for England one day for the sole purpose of visiting Oxford—Newman's Oxford. And in Newman's Oxford he was poignantly reminded of José Maria when he chanced to see two youthful English boys in cap and gown overflowing with loving friendship that seemed to him Platonic in the best sense of the word—Platonic and affectionate. He had witnessed a demonstration of pure, affectionate friendship, untouched by vice.

19

PAULO discovered in the old city of Recife many things that had remained unchanged since the days of his boyhood and adolescence, as well as a good many modern innovations. Some of the latter pleased him; others he found abominable. In Rafael's Hat Store in the Rua Nova—which had changed its name to the Rua Barão da Vitória, but was still known by the old one—he saw men's hats exactly like the English hats worn in France, and hats for ladies and little girls, including bonnets and chapelines, adorned with aigrettes and plumes from Brazilian birds. The doctor with the widest reputation was still Dr. Adrião, who occupied a second-floor office in the Rua do Queimado. Patients also flocked to Chaves's Homeopathic Laboratory. Paulo took a great liking to Mendonça, a dancing master to rich families who had hired an instructor named Batista to teach their children. From the fees charged to wealthy families, Mendonça could afford to give lessons free to poor children. Free dancing lessons for poor children! No one in France would have thought of that. How very Brazilian it was!

Just as in his childhood, the French Pharmacy dominated the drug trade, and Prealle and Company was still the leading vendor of musical instruments. Both establishments had opened their doors in his grandfather's day. Prealle sold not only violins, flutes, and clarinets, which Paulo had loved to admire when he accompanied his mother as a child to the music store on the Rua Nova to buy piano music, but also ivory billiard cues and balls. Paulo had learned the game as a youngster, in the billiard room which his father had installed as a sort of masculine counterpart to his mother's feminine sewing room.

Quantities of European drugs were still shipped to Brazil, particularly from France. Some of these Paulo had never seen in Paris: *Dr. Dumont's preparation for blenorrhea, for example; Robin's Iron Peptonate, for anemia and loss of vitality, or the same Robin's Pepto-Kola, for impotence. Others were well known in Europe: Vichy stomach pills; Vittel water; Girard dentifrices; Chorol Marye.*

France was well represented in Brazil through its medicines, some of which had beautiful names—*Cascarine Leprince* was one—or difficult or pedantic ones, all of which had to compete with those of the indigenous herbs and tinctures, some sonorous, others tongue-twisting and full of native *y*'s. Then there were the medicines prepared in Brazilian laboratories by apothecaries who were learning to be pharmacists. These drugs had been given names that were equally pedantic and equally full of *y*'s, but which were exotic instead of native: *Eupeptic Elixir, Phosphate Chlorhydrate of Calcium, and Chlorhydrate-Pepsic Elixir were mixed by Brazilian chemists in their laboratories.*

The greatest rivals of the European medicines, with their names so romantic and enticing that as a child Paulo had thought they sounded almost like women's names, were now, he noticed, *those made from Brazilian plants and recommended to their patients by homeopaths, including Dr. Sabino. There was Electrol, an unguent for burns; Izinius, for skin disorders, including those caused by syphilis; Poligonum, for hemorrhoids; Elacodendron, for sores and throat infections; Balsamina, a cough medicine; Novrosina, for St. Vitus's dance, hysteria, and nervous disorders; Dermonlina, for psoriasis, scabies, and herpes; and Myrística, for women's complaints.* Those names, too, were as sweet and sonorous as the names of women one loved, Paulo thought. The imported medicines would have to look lively to defend themselves from their Brazilian competitors even when it came to high-sounding names, which were as important a factor in selling medicine as they were in selling perfume. A French perfume manufacturer had once told him that he sometimes found it easier to invent a new perfume than to find a suggestive name for it.

One afternoon when Paulo had gone out to feast his Frenchified South American eyes on what was new in old Recife and what was still Brazilian and uncorrupted, he came across a shop called The Corsair. It was filled with imported furniture, and Paulo sadly noted the invasion of so-called Austrian furniture, which was beginning to take the place of the far finer native jacarandá and vinhático. Another invasion had also commenced: that of the iron bedstead. The very Brazilian china spittoons were still in fashion, as showy and garishly colored as ever. Some of them were painted a poetic pink, scandalously trimmed with gilt. Next to them stood urinals, the lids of which were also painted in clashing colors and poetic motifs. He asked the price of one: it was thirty-five hundred cruzeiros. Competing with them were ugly cedar toilets for nine thousand cruzeiros which were dreadful but modern. Paulo could not restrain himself from letting out a silent, heartfelt hurrah for the urinals. On the other hand, grass mattresses still kept the lead over those stuffed with horsehair. Paulo was sure that grass mattresses were much more hygienic in the Brazilian climate.

Another Brazilian touch that Paulo noticed and was amused by was that the buns served to him at breakfast were called either *"Nabuco buns" or "José Mariano buns." It was the same with cigarettes: they bore names of political heroes of the day. There were also cigarettes named after Dom Vital and buns named after Portela,* and in the home of a Catholic or a Conservative, those were the cigarettes that were smoked and the buns that were eaten at breakfast. *The cafés, too, sold buns and cigarettes according to their political preferences: some sold only Nabuco cigarettes and José Mariano buns, while others specialized in Portela buns and Dom Vital cigarettes.* It was a sign of the passionate interest that Brazilians were beginning to take in politics. Paulo did discover, on the Rua da Imperatriz, a café called Petrópolis which seemed apolitical, where he sometimes went to enjoy a dish of sherbet made from tropical fruit or sip a refreshing drink to the sound of Brazilian and foreign tunes played on the piano. He was soon informed, however, that even Brazilian music was saturated with politics: there were *march tunes named after José Mariano and others named after Nabuco,* exactly like the buns and the cigarettes.

The name heard most often on the lips of Recife's inhabitants was still, perhaps, that of Nabuco. But the fact that Nabuco, an abolitionist, had sided with the monarchy just as the Republic had suddenly triumphed, was turning Quincas the Handsome into a sort of lifeless statue without a future. More than one friend of Paulo's father had lamented, in conversations with the young doctor, the fact that the still-youthful Nabuco was becoming a relic simply because he had not been able, as one of these men explained, to keep pace with the "march of progress." It was a great pity, he had added, because Brazil did not have another such genius as Nabuco, unless it was Ruy.[1] Martins Júnior was a babe at the breast com-

[1] The great liberal statesman and jurist Ruy Barbosa, born in Bahia in 1849, was a member of the imperial Parliament as a progressive liberal deputy. An advocate of federalism and reforms in education and the treatment of slaves, he became noted for his intellectual courage and erudition. After the monarchy was overthrown in 1889, he was appointed Minister of the Interior for the new Republic. The presidentialist constitution of 1891, modeled on that of the United States, was almost entirely of his authorship.

Exiled to London by President Floriano Peixoto for his protests against the restriction of civil liberties, he published

pared to the giant of Maçangana.[2] If Paulo could only have heard *the speech about "the Pernambuco Fatherland" which Nabuco had pronounced in Recife shortly before May 13th!*[3] *It had taken place on a Sunday, and had been a benefit for Judge Freitas's family.* What eloquence, and what wisdom! The devil of it was that Nabuco was still a monarchist. It was a pity. With all his genius, he could not or would not keep pace with the march of progress!

Nabuco. It was Nabuco's name that Paulo, returning to Recife, heard pronounced more frequently than that of anyone else in public life. "It rhymes with Pernambuco," the elder Tavares had remarked more than once. Paulo surprised himself mechanically rhyming Nabuco with Pernambuco.

Even Dona Sinhá's brother, who was grumpy and

---

a defense of Captain Alfred Dreyfus which antedated that of Zola. Returning to Brazil in 1895, he was elected to the Federal Senate, where he served almost uninterruptedly until his death in 1923.

Ruy Barbosa campaigned brilliantly but unsuccessfully for the presidency of the Republic in 1909, and again in 1919. His speech on the juridical concept of neutrality, given at the University of Buenos Aires in 1916, was one of the decisive factors that led Brazil to break off relations with Germany.

As the Brazilian delegate to the World Peace Conference of 1907 at The Hague, Ruy Barbosa achieved international recognition with his eloquent thesis in defense of the equality of nations. He was elected to the World Court of Justice, of which he was a founder, in 1912.

[2] Joaquim Nabuco.

[3] The date of the freeing of the slaves in 1888.

crotchety like every good Wanderley, had a certain weakness for Joaquim Nabuco as well as for Dom Vital, different though the two great men were.

A Wanderley who had less admiration for Nabuco than Dona Sinhá's brother, Chico Canary—very old and feeble now (Luzia had died of a festering ulcer in her chest)—told Paulo he had never seen a more memorable arrival than Nhô Quim's in '85.

It was in December, 1885. Nabuco was convalescing from yellow fever and had been brought to Recife from the Court at Rio in an English ship. An excited multitude was there to welcome him at the landing stage. The provincial governor, with a pettiness regretted even by his followers, refused to give permission for military bands to be present to stir up the enthusiasm of the crowd. Each person would have to whistle his own tune to accompany the shouts of "Viva Nabuco!" Three cutters went out to the English packet boat to welcome him. One was full of men from the Nova Emancipadora abolitionist society; another held members of the Ave Libertas society; the third carried tradespeople. Two other boats joined the cutters. Thus escorted, Nabuco stepped onto the gangplank. Men in the crowd elbowed one another; each wanted to be the first to see what ravages the fever had made in Quincas's face. It was rumored that the disease had disfigured his good looks; and Joaquim Nabuco's good looks were, together with his genius, his wisdom, and his social reformer's ardor, a sort of patrimony of the citizens of Pernambuco. So great was their anxiety that as Nabuco's cutter approached the dock, the huzzahs stopped. Hardly a word broke the hush. Thus Nabuco was welcomed, in almost total silence—the silence that falls in the presence of the grave illness of someone dearly loved. Silently the crowd accompanied Nabuco to the Praça do Campo Santo, where he entered the headquarters of the abolitionist society and stepped out onto the balcony to make his speech. At that moment a vehicle approached in which a little girl unfurled a banner embroidered with the emblem of a sun haloed with brilliant rays, symbolizing Freedom. Below her were an Indian boy and an African girl. Nabuco spoke from the veranda and was applauded. Then followed a speech by Thomaz de Aquino Pereira and verses in praise of Nabuco recited by a child. José Mariano was the next to speak. The little girl who had been chosen as the symbol of Freedom went to the balcony where Nabuco was standing and pinned to his coat a gold medal with the banner of 1817 on one side and a laudatory inscription to him on the other. Chico Canary had seen the medal, and he also remembered that printed copies *of a poem by a certain Senhor Gamba, dedicated to Nabuco and José Mariano, had been thrown to the crowd like a shower of confetti. Nabuco descended from the balcony and, at the urging of the crowd, accompanied it on foot as far as the Rua do Imperador. It was an extremely enthusiastic but at the same time very orderly demonstration—which did not prevent the provincial government from taking military precautions against the abolitionists, who were joyfully*

*celebrating the return of the beloved idol whom a fever
had so nearly taken from them.*

"He was rather thin," Chico Canary said of Nabuco,
"and a little pale." But no one doubted that the air of
Pernambuco would bring him back to health and restore
the fine bearing of the vigorous Brazilian who, in Chico
Wanderley's opinion—and how he harped on the subject!
—should have done his part to improve the race by pro-
creating little Brazilians of various shades, every one of
whom would have been marked with their father's virile
beauty. Let others exalt the orator, the politician, the social reformer, the diplomat, the abolitionist in Nhô Quim
of Maçangana. What Chico Canary saw when he looked
at him was the potential stud horse who had failed to
carry out his most important mission: that of siring
healthy, good-looking mestizos.

Paulo, recalling that in the days of his early youth the
theater had held as important a place as politics in the
life of Recife's intelligentsia, asked his friends for theatrical news. He was told that *hardly any plays had been
staged in Recife since Apolônia Pinto's last season.* A sur-
feit of politics had taken their place, and instead of dramatic theater there were gymnasts and acrobats. *A certain Juanita Palacios was all the rage.* There was no
theater left, only circuses.

*Regattas in the gasworks basin were also very fashion-
able.* Perhaps it was the English influence, as one of
Paulo's Recife friends remarked deprecatingly. A Francophile, he was disdainful of circuses and regattas and re-

gretted that dramatic theater as well as opera seemed to have gone into a decline with the advent of the Republic. The only distinguished singer who had come to Recife lately was *a German named Emmy von Orway.*

One thing that had not declined was Carnival, which continued to reign in all its undiminished splendor. Its songs were now full of praise for the Republic. "What could be more Brazilian than Carnival?" asked Paulo's anti-British friend. The English found Brazilian Carnival revels barbarous, even indecent. A Recife newspaper, however (*The Reporters' Club*), had retorted in words of one syllable, as follows: "*The insipid austerity of the English was not made for those born and bred under ardent tropical skies, where all that surrounds them is smiling and festive. Away with these clouds of British melancholy, these scruples from grumbling moralists. . . ."*

The Francophile went on to reminisce about Carnivals he had enjoyed as a boy, when dousings from water-filled limes and basins had often resulted in bad colds and even consumption; when masked revelers had made mockery of the Religious Question and even of Dom Vital. He remembered having seen one of these masked figures, not in a bishop's dress—that was not allowed—but wearing a purple soutane and pretending to smear his long black beard with brilliantine which he made the gesture of taking from a huge jar. The bearded figure was teetering on high-heeled shoes: women's shoes. It was a caricature of Dom Vital. There were some who swore that the idea for the parody had come from a friend of Monsignor Pinto de

Campos, on whom Dom Vital, with that fearless disre-
gard for consequences which Paulo had so admired in the
Capuchin bishop, *had imposed the penalty of suspension
ex informata,* without a thought for the monsignor's prestige.

While walking through the streets of São José, with its
old two-story houses in which barons and rich sugar
planters had resided in bygone days, Paulo thought of
those Carnivals of his boyhood, which he had usually
chosen to spend in São José rather than in the center of
the city. José Maria had gone out with him during one
Carnival, not without repeated admonitions from Dona
Sinhá. Paulo, disguised in a domino, had felt rather ridiculous. Missy's mother had dressed him in the costume of
a pierrot, which had only accentuated his air of childish
forlornness.

The young man remembered another Carnival when
he had gone hopping along the sidewalks that people in
Recife called "chicken livers" because of their pattern,
with a couple of mischievous devils, the Moreiras, who
lived in the Pátio de Têrço and were known all over São
José as "hot-footers" because of the pranks they played in
Recife street Carnivals. He had heard that the Moreiras
were no longer living; they had both died of typhus. Now,
instead of "hot-footers" they were two mournful skeletons
lying in Santo Amaro Cemetery with their feet together.
How many other Carnival comrades, thought Paulo, were
now lying underground, no longer able to dance or jump
up and down? It was sad to realize, after each Carnival

had passed, how many revelers had died and would never see another.

Paulo thought of Joca the Barber, who had had a great success in one Carnival when Paulo had been a child by striding through the streets dressed as Death, with a menacing scythe in his hand. That same year, around April, Joca had caught a disease that had carried him off to Santo Amaro in a black casket from the firm of Agra. Paulo had seen it as it left the barber's house covered by the conventional purple flowers and carried by other barbers because the dead man had left no relatives to be pallbearers.

Rumor had it that Joca was a virgin. Taciturn, wrapped up in his own thoughts all the rest of the year, he always wore a disguise during Carnival. Sometimes he was a clown, sometimes a giant head, and that last year he had been Death. Paulo recalled that the barbers were a tight-knit group in Recife and, for some reason, full of the spirit of Carnival. More than a month beforehand every year, the barber shops were filled with masks, boxes of paint-filled tubes, and sacks of confetti.

The story that made the rounds on street corners where every Negro woman with her brazier had steady customers for her fried fish or tapioca, and in the pharmacies and other shops frequented by gossiping men, was that Joca should never have been buried in a black coffin with purple flowers. His coffin should have been blue, sky-blue. For no one doubted the virginity of the barber who, for three days every year, transformed himself into the strange, sensational, even macabre Bohemian known to all of Sãn José, but during the rest of the year was only Joca the Barber, a frowning, taciturn man who shaved the faces of his clients in silence as if he were not a barber at all, but a mute. A deaf-mute, in fact; for he never laughed at the indecent stories his customers told about depraved monks, impotent Englishmen, or amarelinhos who accomplished incredible feats without even looking like men.

As Paulo passed Joca's old barbershop in the Pátio do Têrço, he was reminded of something his neighbor, Manoel the Portugee, had told him when he had been a young lad and had just caught his first venereal disease. One day Manoel had helped the barber out of a nasty predicament as both of them hurriedly crossed the Ruo do Fogo. It was raining, and the women did not have many customers. Some of them were standing in doorways and others on their balconies, smoking and calling out curses and obscenities to one another. Just then a saucy mulatto girl caught sight of Joca and shouted: "Here comes Joca the fairy, folks! Here comes the wise guy!"

A cacophony of shouts and catcalls from the women followed this remark. Every one of them shouted some insult at the poor barber. "Come on up, Joca, I'll take off your maidenhead!" "Never been with a woman, Joca! Ain't you ashamed!" "Ain't you fooled around enough already, you damn panty-waist!"

Joca kept on walking, pretending it had nothing to do with him. But no one was fooled: it was Joca the prostitutes were after. Manoel the Portugee could keep silent no longer. As he conspicuously frequented the brothels and in that particular at least the finger of scorn could not be pointed at him, he let fly with such vile and colorful language, in such a fearfully loud voice—as though he wanted his voice to reach "from Tras-os-Montes [4] to the Atlantic Ocean," as he told Paulo afterward in his stentorian bellow—that the women held their tongues. Not that Manoel would not have given anything to see his friend Joca suddenly turn into a frenzied male, run up to one of those balconies, and make at least one of those confounded women moan with pain, not pleasure, until she begged the barber for mercy: "For your sainted mother's sake, Seu Joca! For your sainted mother's sake!" For Joca had the reputation, in São José, of having the biggest male organ in Recife.

Joca. The Moreiras. Carnivals in São José. How fleeting it all had been, except the water. Recife had more water than land. Water dominated people's lives, not only in Recife but in much of the rest of Brazil. And water was life.

Walking along the Rua da Aurora, Paulo gazed at the river as he could not remember ever having gazed at it before going to Europe. In the waters of his beloved river he caught a glimpse of all that tied him most tightly to Brazil when he was away from it. It was not only the river of his Recife childhood that bound him to Brazil

[4] Literally, Behind the Mountains; inland province of northern Portugal.

when he was in Europe; it was the water itself. Hadn't a French geographer, hearing that he was from Pernambuco, told him that he was a native of the Brazilian Sahara where a drought had killed off practically the whole population in 1877? Paulo, seeing the Capibaribe River again, smiled at the thought of the French geographer. Once more he realized how different from the image of an arid land was the picture of Brazil which he carried in his mind. On the contrary, it was that of a country filled almost to overflowing with water—waterfalls like the ones on the plantations of his relatives, where he had bathed as a boy with cousins and Negro boys, naked and shouting; water in the inland creeks; water in the ocean, breaking on the reefs; flood waters inundating the back yards, washing away cabins, even daring to enter the drawing rooms of the rich and climb up the fat, majestic legs of the untouchable grand pianos, those sacred, enormous black pianos with snow-white keys and silver lamps which no child was ever permitted to touch with dirty fingers. Dirty, filthy water that ravaged the well-tended gardens of Recife in the great floods that Paulo had witnessed, invading mansions like that of his uncle Afonso in Madalena, destroying fine rose bushes, killing aristocratic plants, and reducing delicate lilies to plebeian weeds.

The nostalgic memories that had tormented Paulo most in Europe had been those in which the image of his mother, his godmother, his nursemaid, his father, all his people, as well as Carnivals of days long past, had mingled with his memories of water. Waves crashing on the reefs, sliding along the edges of the wharves, tumbling rudely against docks and banks, flooding the lowlands where wild grass and bindweed grew, playing with the stones, letting themselves be tamed by ragged children, luring girls with loose hair to fling themselves into the water after they had been ruined by Don Juans who went up the river in romantic boats, singing serenades in the moonlight. Paulo had a recollection of having gone up the river in a boat himself, on a moonlit night, to serenade some girls in Ponte d'Uchoa. It had all been very romantic; the young men singing in the boat and the girls listening to their troubadours at a distance, from the second-floor veranda, an enormous porch that faced the river. All they could see of the girls was their shadows, for there was no gaslight in the house, only votive oil lamps kept burning all night before the statues of the saints.

Water again . . . water had always predominated in the nostalgic yearning for Brazil which Paulo had felt in Europe. Not once during his long absence had Brazil appeared to him in memory as the dry, arid, waterless country of which the French geographer had spoken. He remembered hearing dreadful stories about the drought of '77, a sinister year for all Brazilian ears. The scourge of '77, however, had affected only the backlands and the men who lived in them. It was true that the calamity had shaken all the rest of vast Brazil and forced its other inhabitants to think of their brothers in the backlands. It had also made those other Brazilians more than ever sure that they were favored by God with a blessed abundance of water in the oceans, the rivers, and the waterfalls. Maternal water; motherly water; water peopled by water sprites. Water that was almost always man's protector, almost never his enemy.

And then there were the playful, lascivious, joyful, festive, frenzied waters of the great Brazilian Carnivals of Rio and Recife. Paulo had never spent a Carnival in Rio, but he knew that the carioca Carnivals rivaled those of Recife; that they were Dionysian, Afro-Brazilian, like those of Recife.

20

"WELL, BOY, I've been reading some of the things you've written. *Pedrinho from Japaranduba* showed them to me. You know *Pedrinho, the one who married our cousin Laura.* You're pretty smart, and you put in a lot of words that your old backwoods cousin from Serinhaém never heard of. But mixed up with all those hard words there's some others that made me see a lot of things I hadn't thought of before. You've got talent. And talent's not so common in a Wanderley. Wanderleys are sly, they're clever, they're foxy. But talent's not our strong point. I always say a Wanderley's only a genius if you compare him with a Correia de Oliveira. Zemaria? That little priest knew so much he used to scare me sometimes. He didn't get his brains from Sinhá or our parents. My father was a country boy who never got taken in by any city slicker, but he wasn't what you'd call brilliant, and he didn't have much use for books. The only thing he read was the newspaper and once in a while an almanac or the *Luso-Brazilian Souvenirs.* What he really set store by was a good shot of white lightning, a good horse, a good cockfight, and, just between you and me, a good-looking mulata. Maybe Zemaria got some of his brains from his father's side of the family. His father was a real caboclo from Amazonas. And Zemaria was a little like Dom Vital in the way he looked at things. Dom Vital might have had some Indian blood in him; a lot of people thought so. I wouldn't be surprised if Dom Vital was descended from that smart Indian woman, Maria-Jump-Over-the-Creek."

These words were spoken to me one day by old Gaspar, Dona Sinhá's brother. He had been tippling and his tongue had been loosened, though he still drawled when he spoke.

"Well, young doctor, you're still a boy, not like me. I've been around too long already, and besides, I'm just a backwoodsman from Serinhaém. You're young, and you've had an education. And I'll tell you something: you'll see the day when Masonic lodges are going to be as scarce in this country of ours as shops selling oil lamps or ladies' bustles are today. And you're going to see the Church stronger than it is today, with more priests like Dom Vital. Real priests, not those imperial flunkies who used to live on chicken and port wine and say mass and baptize Christians as if they were working for the government, and have all the strumpets they wanted, like that famous one from Ceará who had three of 'em and was always hankering for young girls to warm his bones."

After I had listened in silence, but in some surprise, to the anticlericalist who had done all he could to keep his nephew from becoming a priest but was now defending the Church and Dom Vital and the priests whom he called "Dom Vital's kind," the lord of Olindeta added in his nasal Wanderley voice, in which there had been curiously preserved something that reminded me of a reformationist of Luther's day:

"Zemaria could have been another Dom Vital today. As for being skinny and having a girl's feet and a woman's hands—well, so did that little monk from Goiana. But what that puny little monk did get away from when he was still a boy was all his mother's and nursemaid's petting. He would have been spoiled for life if he hadn't gone to Europe and had to do work that was niggers' work here in Brazil. He even had to sweep the kitchen floor and clean out the old monks' latrines—French latrines. And you know, young fellow, that Frenchman's shit smells like the devil in person, it's not like caboclo crap. It really stinks. Whenever there were French engineers staying at the big-house in Olindeta, the niggers knew enough to cover up their noses so as not to faint dead away from the stink of those gringos' shit."

Repeating what he had said before, old Wanderley went on belying my supposition that there lingered on in him, out of sheer inertia as a descendant of Protestants, a half-Protestant Catholic:

"Doubt that the Church is God's church? I don't doubt it. I know I've told you I don't know how many times that I don't go along with prayers and novenas and such, because that kind of thing is for women and priests; and I'm not a woman or a priest. But that the church belongs to God—I don't doubt that for a minute. No man in this world can get the better of the Church. No man, no government, nobody. Anyone who saw what I did, who saw what the fight between the Church and the Masons was like, knows what I'm talking about. It looked as if pretty soon there'd be nothing left of the Church. All you could see were Masons. Masons in the government, Masons in the clergy, Mason priests gnawing away at the Church from the inside out. Then all of a sudden the Church turns up with a little Goiana amarelo to defend it like a real man. Don't let anybody tell you different—that Dom Vital was a he-man caboclo. He was sort of a cabeleira [1] serving God, only his hair was in his beard. And you know what? He was just skin and bones when the monks took him to Europe. Puny, pale, and spoiled by his mother. Just like Zemaria. They say, though, that the cold weather in Europe and the hard work in that French convent made that Goiana caboclo show them what kind of man he was. They say the old monks made a slave of him to take the prissiness out of him. They made him sweep the kitchen floor and clean out latrines, and he'd do it all without a murmur, as obedient as a lamb, and kiss the little medal of the Virgin that he wore around his neck. And it turned out all right. When he came back from Europe, he was the bravest son-of-a-gun anyone around here had ever seen. Just when it looked as though the Masons were about to finish off the Church, darned if that little bearded latrine cleaner and kitchen-floor sweeper didn't leap up like a lion and win the day. Look at how strong the Church is today; stronger than it was thirty years ago,

[1] Long-haired man; also, in the Brazilian northeast, an attacker, a brigand.

and all because of that little Goiana amarelo. Do you
know, young fellow, what my nephew needed to turn him
into another Dom Vital? He needed to spend a while in
Europe a long way from Sinhá, doing what Vital had to
do: cleaning out latrines and sweeping out Frenchmen's
kitchens. It's a hard thing to say, but that's the way
things are in this world. That's the way life is. I'll bet you
anything you like that if Friar Vital had stayed here he
would have been as fussy and old-maidish as José Maria,
with the boys calling the poor thing Missy, too. Cazuza de
Wunda told me about Friar Vital when he was still called
Antônio. He said he never was the kind of boy who liked
to ride horseback or run after oxen—he was a peculiar
sort of a boy. His father used to say it was a shame that
Maria-Jump-Over-the-Creek wasn't alive to give him riding lessons. You know who Maria-Jump-Over-the-Creek
was. *She was a cabocla from the tribe that brought Councilor João Alfredo* [2] *into the world.* She was a devil of a
cabocla. A St. George in skirts.

"What I always say is," Dona Sinhá's brother added in
the philosophical tone of a conscientious old man confessing to a priest or a young confidant, "that I'm not
much for praying; that praying's for women. But don't

[2] Councilor João Alfredo Correia de Oliveira (1835–1919),
Pernambuco lawyer and statesman, shared the leadership of
the Conservative Party in the last decade of the reign of Dom
Pedro II with Baron Cotegipe. After several years as an imperial minister, he assumed the presidency of the next-to-last
imperial cabinet in 1888, the year slavery was abolished in
Brazil.

212

think I set everything male above everything female. Yes, I'm a rough customer and a brute; but a brute who's willing to admit that if there were no women and churches, but just brutes like me riding broncos and planting sugar cane in the ground, this Brazil of ours wouldn't be what it is today. Look at Dom Vital. When he gave up the name Antônio and took the name Vital, he turned into a priest who accomplished what he did with hardly a bit of help from anyone. He wore a skirt and decked himself out in lace, and as long as his name was Antônio he was just an Antoninho nobody paid any attention to because he was so little and insignificant; but look what he did as a priest. No one can hold out against priests, women, or the Church. They're stronger than any of us he-men, with all our boasting and all our silver spurs."

The priest's uncle, in a philosophical vein, added in his drawling Serinhaém Wanderley voice: "Monarchy—republic—it doesn't make any difference. What Brazil needs is good government. In other words, it doesn't need good republicans or good monarchists, but good Brazilians. It's like that Masonry business, neither good nor bad. What the Masons ought to do is stop sticking their noses into politics and practice more charity. And the same goes for the Church: it ought to act more like a Church. That fellow with the beard was right. But I don't know anything about that; I'm not a praying man. Praying's for priests and for women. But as for respecting a real priest when I see one, that I do. There's not a Mason in this world who can accomplish half of what a real, honest-to-goodness priest can do. It's true, I didn't want Zemaria to be a priest, because I wanted to make an Olindeta planter out of him. I wanted him to spend his time yelling orders to the men loading sugar cane, not hearing old women's confessions. But that doesn't mean I don't respect a genuine priest when I meet up with a Dom Vital."

21

FIRST his father's absence, and now the absence of José Maria. Why had he died so soon—that strange boy who had perturbed Paulo's adolescence and troubled his Catholic conscience more than any woman?

Paulo became conscious of a selfish conviction that what had happened was for the best: that it was better not to have come back to Brazil to find an adult, banal José Maria; a bureaucratic, humdrum priest saying mass and presiding at weddings. Surely it was far better that the boy's image should have remained innocent of the corroding action of time—of time and of the tropics. There was no doubt a fairly large dose of egoism in the attitude of this reader of Newman. Paulo verified, nevertheless, after sounding the innermost depths of his feelings, that José Maria's absence had indeed affected him in just this way.

Paulo went to São José do Ribamar and walked by Dona Sinhá's house as though he were a stranger. The Square was just as it had been in José Maria's boyhood days. Angular shadows turned the courtyard into a poverty-stricken stage set for the performance of some provincial drama set in a lethargic village. The declining sun left some houses in almost total darkness, while others still caught the brilliant sunlight.

Paulo saw children at play: the eternal children of São José, who still had not learned to play anywhere but in the streets and plazas, even when their houses had back yards. Tavares walked by a group of them, who interrupted their play to let him pass. They were playing puss-in-the-corner. The sauciest of the boys called out: "Stop playing so that boy can get by!" Another corrected him: "Boy, nothing. He's a man!" This natural objectivity on the part of a boy of the Recife streets made Tavares sharply conscious of what he was: no longer a youth, but an adult. A man.

Tavares saw another boy flying all by himself a paper kite like the kites José Maria had flown. Other, more gregarious children were spinning tops.

None of the children was another José Maria. There was not one whose eyes had the sweetness that José Maria's eyes had had. The much-traveled Tavares, who had now come home again to his own province, had seen such sweetness in only two other places. One was in Italy, in the eyes of certain figures of angels, John the Baptists, and St. Louis Gonzagas that had been painted by the Old Masters in the golden epoch when the Church had inspired a kind of art which had died long ago, at least that part of it which was ephebic, purified of paganism. The other was in Spain, in Avila. Paulo had been returning slowly from the convent where St. Teresa had lived, in a sort of rapture, so deeply moved had he been by the

Catholic mystery, when a little Spanish boy had passed close by him—a grave and mystical child whose eyes had the same strange sweetness as José Maria's. The thought had occurred to Paulo that St. Teresa, before she became a saint, may have had just such glowing eyes, angelic and yet expressive, too, of human love at its most tender.

Paulo had kissed many Frenchwomen in the course of his seven years in Europe—Frenchwomen, Belgians, Italians, Spaniards, even an Englishwoman. None of their kisses, however, had left in his memory a sensation as intense as that he had received one day in school from the lips of José Maria. Only he remembered the instant when in his audacity as an older adolescent male he had kissed the innocent boy almost violently. While the childlike mouth seemed to receive the sensual warmth of his own without shrinking, José Maria's eyes had gazed at the aggressor in astonishment, as though he did not understand that expression of love. It was as though his eyes belonged to one person and his mouth to another, as though his eyes understood only the friendship in Paulo's intensely affectionate gesture, while his mouth responded to the other, the sensual, love.

The strange experience that had forged such peculiarly affectionate bonds between Paulo and Dona Sinhá's son, in which Paulo had discovered, in a boy devoted to God and the saints and deeply attached to his mother, a pleasure that was different from those which he had already enjoyed, like any normal Brazilian male, with women of various hues on bed, pallet, couch, or hammock, had haunted Paulo in Europe. While there, he had often tried to discover in the art of writers and painters of the Church other expressions of the same enchanting grace, which no doubt had its origin in Greece but had acquired a Catholic mysticism expressed in portraits of adolescent angels and youthful saints. Paulo recalled having read in Pater—Newman's books had led him to those of Pater, and then to a visit to Oxford to pay homage to the two great Englishmen—that the word *mystic,* derived from the Greek, signified "closed." According to some scholars it was the mouth that was closed, so that the mystic would not be subject to worldly contacts through the utterance of words regarding matters better meditated upon than spoken of; while according to the followers of Plato, it was the eyes rather than the mouth which should remain closed, as by closing his eyes the mystic would perceive more clearly the mysteries within himself. Be that as it may, the saints and angels limned by Italian painters were invariably given eyes like those of adolescents, open to the world, and mouths that were sometimes very human—the mouths of ephebic servants of God. Without those parted lips and wide-open eyes, the grace and beauty of these figures would have been less convincing as art. The Church, in the days of its greatness, had welcomed every form of beauty which harmonized with its doctrines, including the extraordinary beauty of angels, who were neither male nor female but belonged to what might be termed by the Church a third, mystical sex.

Paulo went down to the beach where he and José Maria had often talked to fishermen in the old days. None of the half-breed fishermen they had known was there, but as Paulo repassed Dona Sinhá's house on his way back, he saw one of the sunburned old men who had told them stories about Iemanjá and the mermaids in a low voice when José Maria was out of his mother's sight. He introduced himself to the old man and was glad he had done so, for instead of sadly recalling the past, the fisherman spoke of happier, more recent things: that the sea had been kind to the poor people lately; that the catches were the best he remembered seeing since he had come to manhood; and that he had just sold to Dona Sinhá's Negro cook a "girl's leg" horse mackerel that was so tempting it would have to be seen to be believed. Of the past, he said of José Maria only this: "I never met a young fellow like him!"

Paulo was on the point of announcing himself to Dona Sinhá's Negro servant—"Tell Dona Sinhá it's Dr. Paulo to see her"—but on second thought he decided that it would be better to save his visit to José Maria's mother for another day.

He strolled aimlessly about the streets, the old familiar streets, of São José. Time hardly seemed to have touched its buildings, for the most part. There were the same houses with the same balconies and the very same churches. The very people he encountered, even though they might not be the acquaintances with whom he and José Maria had talked when they went out walking, looked so much the same that they might as well have been. He introduced himself to some of them; others seemed to think he was a foreigner.

Although some of these renewed acquaintances brought back poignant memories of Dona Sinhá's son, such memories could not prevail over Paulo's conviction that it was on the whole better not to have been greeted in Brazil, after an absence of so many years in Europe, by an adult, banal José Maria—unless, he thought to himself more than once, he might have become a real saint after all. But it did not seem very likely to Paulo that there were any saints in Brazil.

22

"TELL DONA SINHÁ that Dr. Paulo is here," said Paulo to the servant in the old house on the Square of São José do Ribamar. It was the servant he had seen talking to the fisherman several days before. She disappeared into the interior of the house while Paulo waited.

"Missus says to tell you to come right in, Seu Doutor!" said the Negro maid. As Paulo entered the sitting room, Dona Sinhá appeared in the hall as though she had been expecting him. Although she was so profoundly unhappy that she looked like a different woman, time had not yet altered her expression or her gait. Both had retained their youthfulness.

Sinhá shed tears as she embraced her son's dearest friend. Yes, she knew that God and Our Lady had more right to José Maria than she had. But she had always counted on dying in the arms of her priest son, not on seeing the little priest die in her sinner's arms.

Dona Sinhá had not changed in relation to her son. Although a sinner in her own eyes because she was not a saint, she still thought of herself as the mother of a saint. Paulo was grieved to see the black-garbed aristocrat shedding plebeian tears, sobbing and wailing, almost shrieking. The mother's sorrow was so nakedly apparent in those tears that it seemed a reproach to God and Our Lady for what they had done to her. True, she was a sinner, but she had always been devoted to Our Lord and His Mother, and they had taken her son away from her when he was hardly more than a child. If she was a sinner, Paulo thought, it was only on a very modest scale. She had committed no great sins, only peccadilloes. No mortal sin weighed on her conscience to brand her in the eyes of God and men.

Paulo Tavares proffered a few words to Dona Sinhá, words that he felt were conventional, even banal, as he spoke them, a friend's poor attempt to console a grieving mother. It was at that moment, conscious of being conventional and banal, that Paulo felt a sudden strong desire to take poor Dona Sinhá into his almost filial arms and offer her a love that he just as suddenly realized might mean more to her than that of a quasi-son: that of a husband-son who might be able to take the place, in Dona Sinhá's heart, of the son who had been taken from her, and for him might replace the absurd, impossible love, overflowing with friendship, which had bound him to José Maria.

When Dona Sinhá, dressed all in black, had appeared to him from the shadowy hallway, her fair Wanderley face whiter than ever, Paulo had been struck by her eyes, which were still surprisingly youthful. They were the eyes of the boy who had almost become a priest.

Paulo had always thought Dona Sinhá attractive. Not as beautiful as black Luzia, but pretty enough. Age had not destroyed the charm she had possessed as a young widow. She was still appealing.

In Europe, the fact that Paulo was a South American with a reputation for being wealthy had permitted him to make the intimate acquaintance of really beautiful women —beautiful of face and beautiful of body. It was curious that after so many experiences of that kind, he should now feel that the only woman who could tempt him into marriage was this one: Dona Sinhá. More than anything else, it was because of her still-youthful eyes, whose haunting sweetness evoked in Paulo, to whom she was almost a second mother, feelings that were difficult to explain. He knew, though, that one of them was the memory of the eyes of Sinhá's dead son, to whom he had felt so close.

Dona Sinhá had sobbed in his arms. She was still tearful as she spoke of José Maria and of how his friendship for Paulo had remained unchanged during his last illness in Angelim. In her heart, Dona Sinhá had thought all along, during those terrible days in Angelim, that the person her son longed for most was Paulo; not so much Paulo the doctor as Paulo the friend. Dona Sinhá was sure that her son had resisted his illness only long enough to console her, so that she would not think he had no regrets at leaving his earthly mother for the Mother in Heaven.

Paulo looked attentively at Dona Sinhá as she offered him coffee. Would he have coffee or port wine? Port with a little piece of cake? Paulo chose coffee.

Dona Sinhá still dressed well, according to the austere

pattern of Brazilian widowhood. She avoided trimmings and colors, but she was not insensible to fashion. Furthermore, she knew how to adapt the fashion of the day to her circumstances as a widow of many years, and even to her sorrow as a mother who had only recently lost her only child. For example, the strips of velvet trimming on her aristocratic full skirt matched the velvet cuffs of her tight sleeves and graced her figure, not merely with a touch of mourning, but with an almost religious modesty and lack of ostentation. Paulo remembered having once seen Dona Sinhá, when José Maria was still a child, in a party dress that had lent an unaccustomed luster to the charm of his friend's mother. That had been more than ten years before. He recalled that the dress had been light gray, or perhaps lavender, with pleats edged in black taffeta, and that it had accentuated all of Dona Sinhá's aristocratic charm. It had also emphasized her unhappiness. Paulo had never seen Dona Sinhá except as a sad-eyed woman dressed in mournful blacks, grays, and lavenders. He realized, however, that part of her sadness was a mother's tenderness—the tenderness of a mother who must suffer for her child in order to feel like a woman, a Christian, and a Brazilian. It was this sorrowful tenderness that lent to Dona Sinhá, who was now about forty years of age, a greater charm than she had had in the days when she had been a green and immature young widow who sometimes looked more like her son's older sister than his mother.

Then and there Paulo felt a desire, as romantic as it

was realistic, to tell Dona Sinhá, between sips of the coffee that she had served to him according to the tradition of the house, that he loved her and wished she would consent to be his wife.

He recalled his experiences with European women, almost all of whom had been older than he. He had been the student, considered almost a child by the women who had been his teachers, substitutes for his faraway mother.

The only words that occurred to him with which to express a desire so far outside the patriarchal Brazilian norm—adult men marrying gently reared young girls who were closer to childhood than to womanhood— struck him as inappropriate and absurd. His decision to write a letter to Dona Sinhá the following day was, perhaps, more European than Brazilian.

The rest of the visit was spent in talk about everyday things, particularly those household arts at which Dona Sinhá still excelled. She remarked to Paulo with a touch of irony that now that he was a "Frenchman," he had no doubt lost interest in these ingenuous Brazilian efforts. After all, when it came to art—any kind of art—France was France.

Paulo protested: "I assure you, Dona Sinhá, that we have no reason to envy France when it comes to household arts." Coming amiably down to specifics, he added: "I know this chair cover, for instance, must be your work. One doesn't see exquisite work like this in France."

The truth was that no one in France would have

thought of using armchair covers, much less trimming them with ribbons. The fashion was, in its way, as interesting a "Brazilianism" as the rings worn by university graduates and doctors. Paulo was not always addressed as "Doctor" by people in Brazil; he had become too French to wear the symbolic ring, although his father had given him one with a fine emerald in it. In France rings were meant to be worn by women, never by men.

Tavares observed that the covers of Dona Sinhá's armchairs were beautifully made. Delicate flakes of lace, slightly gathered at the corners, were held together by blue satin ribbons. The edge of the lace was intricately scalloped—extremely difficult to do, Paulo guessed, thinking of the wondrous weaving of the lace-makers of Bruges. With a touch of pride, Dona Sinhá explained, in the French she had learned from the nuns of São José, that the spidery little squares of lace that covered her jacarandá furniture and made it less somber were *filet guipure*—probably poor relations of the laces of Bruges, Tavares thought, though he did not know enough about the subtleties of lace-making to venture an opinion without the risk of being mistaken.

The thought entered Paulo Tavares's mind that Dona Sinhá, invariably dressed in dark colors, had become a sort of dressmaker to her jacarandá armchairs, adorning them with the laces and the blue satin ribbons that ought to have adorned herself or her son: fine lace fit for a priest to wear when saying mass, christening children, or officiating in other solemnities of the Church.

He imagined the charm of that woman—so feminine and so maternal, touched with the autumnal grace with which certain women between forty and fifty are endowed—if she could be dressed in silk again and wear a skirt with flounces and furbelows. With this new vision of Dona Sinhá contrasting with the severe black figure of the woman with whom he had been talking for more than an hour, Paulo took his leave of José Maria's mother, more than ever determined to write to her and beg her to be his wife. Dona Sinhá's answer would determine the course of his future life. Either he would settle in Brazil or he would go on living in France like so many other Brazilians of modest fortune who had taken up residence in Paris and who had always struck Paulo as unhappy ex-Brazilians pretending to be gay Parisians.

23

TAVARES WROTE to Dona Sinhá, begging her to say yes —to say yes without delay. He set down all his reasons and arguments as clearly as he could. Someone who had read the letter informed me that it was "well written, but it sounded as though it had been translated from the French. Tavares no longer looked at things through the eyes of a Brazilian."

24

DONA SINHÁ'S REPLY (I did not read the letter, but was told about it by the same informant who had read Paulo's) was written in her very French handwriting, but there was nothing French about her way of looking at the matter. On the contrary, it was most Brazilian. She could never think of Paulo in any other way than as an older brother of José Maria. She hoped he would be happy in Europe, and that he would not forget to pray for José Maria's soul and for her, Dona Sinhá.

25

THE LAST PERSON with whom I spoke about Dona Sinhá's son was Friar Rosário, in whose arms José Maria had died of consumption in Angelim.

Dona Sinhá had told me how, on the day before he died, José Maria, hot with fever and clinging to her hand, had rambled in his delirium.

"He even talked a little bit of foolishness," my Wanderley relative added.

"Such as . . ."

"He talked about Iemanjá."

"He was thinking of Ribamar."

"Yes. Thinking of Ribamar. But saying 'Mother, Mother, Mother,' over and over."

"He was sorry to leave you, Dona Sinhá."

"And calling on the Mother of God and Men, his patron saint. Sometimes he would let go of my hand and try to open his arms, as if someone else were waiting for him with open arms. 'Can you see the Blessed Mary, my Maria' I asked him, and he smiled. I'm sure he was seeing the Queen of Heaven and Our Lord."

It was odd that Our Lord always came after Mary. Mary was the Supreme Being for Dona Sinhá, and she often called José Maria "my Maria." To his mother he had always been more Maria than José.

"Once my Maria said 'Paulo' in a very low voice. He remembered Paulo to the very last."

On the day of his death, he had confessed and taken communion. His most faithful companion, besides his mother, was Friar Rosário, an Italian Capuchin who had been in Brazil only a short time and whom I met when he was a very old man, not long before he went back to Europe to die in his beloved Naples.

Dona Sinhá had told me that Friar Rosário had been enchanted by "my Maria," and had added: "And when José Maria died, he was the one who cried over the little saint the most, after me. He said: 'What a priest the Church has lost! But the Virgin Mary knows best.'"

Friar Rosário had given Dona Sinhá some verses he had written in his old-fashioned Italian, which Sinhá Wanderley, well taught by the nuns of St. Joseph's, had memorized word for word. I copied down the verses. They were very Franciscan, very tender, and very consoling to a mother who had been as devoted to her son as Dona Sinhá. However, there is no point in transcribing them here.

Friar Rosário saw that there was no trace of sorrow on José Maria's face. He had welcomed death as though he knew that the Virgin Mary would shield him from the horror of mortal decay. The friar smiled, content to serve a Church that protected its innocents at the hour of their death—the innocents who, having virtually no experience of life, accepted almost joyfully the experience of death.

One thing had caused the good friar some surprise: the lips of the almost lifeless young priest, after kissing Dona Sinhá for the last time, had outlined in the air a vain gesture of longing for a kiss from the lips of some-one else. The watching priest observed that his lips had taken on an almost violet pallor. They were so pale that one would have thought them incapable of giving or re-ceiving any but fleshless kisses. Friar Rosário had lifted his Capuchin's crucifix to José Maria's lips; José Maria died kissing it, with Dona Sinhá at his side.

Dona Sinhá, having watched her beloved only son die before her eyes, burst into a storm of weeping, as though she could not understand why such an unbearably heavy cross should be laid upon her so soon. Friar Rosário tried to console her, but at first all his words of comfort were in vain: Dona Sinhá was prostrated by her grief as a mother whose child had been brutally torn from her arms. It was necessary for the Capuchin to remonstrate with her: "What about your faith, madame? Where is your faith, madame? Your faith in God and the Holy Virgin?"

The good Capuchin told me that as José Maria had expired in his arms, he had pronounced the *Nihil inquin-atum*. And partly in his Italianate Latin, partly in Portu-guese, he had turned to the One whom ritual enshrines as *Flame of Everlasting Brightness, Spotless Mirror of Di-vine Majesty, Perfect Image of the Goodness of God*. Let Her receive the beloved youth who had grown up among lilies, and who, even on earth, had belonged more to the Blessed Mary than to anyone on earth. The friar added poetry to the liturgy: *Ave Maris Stella, Dei Mater Alma, Atque semper virgo, Felix Coeli porta. Sumens illud Ave, Gabrielis ore, Funda nos in pace, Mutans Hevae nonem.* And with an Italian's emphasis, he prayed for the son who was now in search of his eternal Mother: *Monstra te esse matrem.*

A NOTE ABOUT THE AUTHOR

GILBERTO DE MELLO FREYRE was born at Recife (Pernambuco) on March 15, 1900. He studied under private tutors and at the Colégio Americano Gilreath in his native city. In 1920 he took a Bachelor of Arts degree at Baylor University in Waco, Texas, and in 1922 an M.A. at Columbia University, where he did graduate work under Franz Boas, Franklin Henry Giddings, Carlton J. H. Hayes, and Edwin R. A. Seligman.

Freyre has been visiting professor or lecturer at many of the leading universities of Europe and America—among them Leland Stanford, Princeton, Columbia, Michigan, San Marcos (Lima), Coimbra (Portugal), King's College (London), the Sorbonne, Heidelberg, Berlin, Cologne, Hamburg, Bonn, and Indiana. Freyre was a member in 1946 of the National Assembly that drew up the present constitution of Brazil. From 1946 to 1950, he served in the Chamber of Deputies and on its Committee on Cultural and Educational Matters. In 1949 he was a delegate, with the rank of Ambassador, from Brazil to the General Assembly of the United Nations.

Earlier books by Gilberto Freyre published in English include *The Masters and the Slaves* (1946; 1956); *New World in the Tropics* (1959); and *The Mansions and the Shanties* (1963).

A NOTE ON THE TYPE

THE TEXT of this book was set in a typeface called Primer, designed by Rudolph Ruzicka for the Mergenthaler Linotype Company and first made available in 1949. Primer, a modified modern face based on Century broadface, has the virtue of great legibility and was designed especially for today's methods of composition and printing.

Primer is Ruzicka's third typeface. In 1940 he designed Fairfield, and in 1947 Fairfield Medium, both for the Mergenthaler Linotype Company.

Ruzicka was born in Bohemia in 1883 and came to the United States at the age of eleven. He attended public schools in Chicago and later the Chicago Art Institute. During his long career he has been a wood engraver, etcher, cartographer, and book designer. For many years he was associated with Daniel Berkeley Updike and produced the annual keepsake for The Merrymount Press from 1911 until 1941.

Ruzicka has been honored by many distinguished organizations, and in 1936 he was awarded the gold medal of the American Institute of Graphic Arts. From his home in New Hampshire, Ruzicka continues to be active in the graphic arts.

This book was composed, printed, and bound by The Kingsport Press, Inc., Kingsport, Tenn. Typography and binding design by George Salter.